3 Little W

Daily Diary Series

By

Thomas K McMillan

I would like to dedicate this book to my beautiful wife Anita and our 3 glorious kids, Kyla, Maddox and Sienna.

Your help and support is never ending for which I am eternally grateful.

Much love,

Thomas Xxxx

We are in a time where less is more in terms of Communication Styles and we are starting to choose emoji's over words. Tom has brilliantly tapped into this evolution and delivered a very modern book to inspire people using phrases despite these changing times.

3 Little Words keeps it short & sweet but also thought provoking and meaningful!

"Well done Tom"!

Anthony Chorlton

Businessman

Thomas's quotes give my day a daily lift and believe they serve as a great reminder to keep our focus on track.

I often share with my team as believe we can all benefit from a bit of motivation in our personal and business lives.

Matt Donnelly

Business Leader

I have always enjoyed reading Thomas's quotes on social media but now with my own daily journal I can personalize what they mean to me every single day, and can reflect back to them later.

Jonathan Andrew

Celebrity Hairdresser & Podcaster

"Today we begin....."

What could this mean for you, what differences can you introduce to your life right now, at this specific stage? This can be the start, this can be the moment when you commit to taking the first step. Today you can take that leap of faith and commit to your journey.

My Day /

_____

_____

_____

_____

_____

_____

_____

_____

_____

_____

_____

"Make your start."

The most difficult thing about any mental or physical exercise is getting started........don't put it off any longer! So often we find going to the gym the hardest part of the exercise, once we've actually started the enjoyment shines through.

My Day /

_____
_____
_____
_____
_____
_____
_____
_____
_____
_____
_____
_____

"I can be........"

How do you see yourself, what do you truly believe you can turn your life into? What Goals do you have in place currently, are they written down, are you dedicated to committing yourself to being who you really can become?

My Day /

_____
_____
_____
_____
_____
_____
_____
_____
_____
_____
_____

"I will suffice."

You have the tools, you are equipped, all that's left is putting it to work! You are good enough, you are talented enough, you require now to mix in the dedication and desire. As you progress self belief builds, the doubts slither away and your inner strength shines through.

My Day /

_____
_____
_____
_____
_____
_____
_____
_____
_____
_____
_____
_____

"It will happen."

If you can develop your self belief, and add to that the effort and work required, of course it will happen for you. This process is one step at a time, anticipating that rocks will emerge in your path but knowing too that you are capable of bypassing them one at a time. This process may take time, but what else will you do with the time anyway?!

My Day /

_____
_____
_____
_____
_____
_____
_____
_____
_____
_____
_____

"I can change."

At times we need to review our thinking and review our actions........and then have the courage to make those changes, whatever they may be. It can be difficult to self assess, and if that's you, get a friend or family member you trust to help you, what do they honestly see that you need to improve or develop to make your Goal(s) reachable?

My Day /

_____
_____
_____
_____
_____
_____
_____
_____
_____
_____
_____

"Live without limitation."

Don't place unnecessary limits upon your life's journey.....only your thinking will hold you back from your capabilities. Our mental approach must be assured first, it'll help us when the going gets tough, and then you'll see how high you can lift the ceiling.

My Day /

_____
_____
_____
_____
_____
_____
_____
_____
_____
_____
_____
_____

"Fulfill your potential."

Don't be sat 20 years down the line talking about what you could have been.........make use of your talents now. This is a one time around gift, we won't be getting the time over. Making mistakes trying is way better than thinking about them sat on your sofa........get out there, fall over even, but get back up and forge ahead, that's what life is all about.

My Day /

_____
_____
_____
_____
_____
_____
_____
_____
_____
_____
_____
_____

"Begin with you."

No one can do it for you, it must 'begin with YOU'. You are the spearhead of this trip, you are primarily who must commit, and you will be the one who is rewarded most. Decide what and who you are trying to become, and focus on developing yourself into that state.

My Day /

_____
_____
_____
_____
_____
_____
_____
_____
_____
_____
_____

"Control your thinking."

If you can control your thinking you WILL control your actions. So often our state of mind let's us down and with that our actions are weakened. Set out your day, start with something both constructive AND positive, you will be amazed at how your day rolls out when you get off to a good start.

My Day /

_____
_____
_____
_____
_____
_____
_____
_____
_____
_____
_____

"Just be you."

Trust in who you are, no falsehoods, no hiding behind a blank face.......just be YOU! This is your personal blog, this is the first part in a long term series where you have the lead role, and the audience are crying out to see the star of the show.

My Day /

_____
_____
_____
_____
_____
_____
_____
_____
_____
_____
_____
_____

"I can succeed."

You must hold on to that inner belief, overcome the obstacles, overcome the challenges, and knowing throughout that it is possible for you. Start your first Goal on a shorter term, feel the joy of your initial achievement, of that target set and target met mentality.

My Day /

_____
_____
_____
_____
_____
_____
_____
_____
_____
_____
_____
_____

"Let's go explore."

Get out there and discover who you are and what you can become. Remember that moment when you had your first day at school, or first day in your first job........the fear, the anxiety......the excitement! It's time to get out and see what the World has to offer, what it can hold for YOU.

My Day /

_____
_____
_____
_____
_____
_____
_____
_____
_____
_____
_____
_____
_____

"Make it happen."

If the door isn't fully yet open then let's kick it down! We have to up the game at times, take a little bit more risk, push ourselves beyond barriers we have built up mentally and even at times, physically. Sometimes we have to lift ourselves somewhat to ensure getting over this little bridge that has presented itself.

My Day /

_____
_____
_____
_____
_____
_____
_____
_____
_____
_____
_____
_____

"Give your all."

Half measures only end in regret, give it everything you've got and you'll never doubt the results. Can you imagine the pain of knowing you could have succeeded if you'd been at your best, if you'd attended every aspect of training, and if you'd outworked your competition when you had the chance?

My Day /

_____
_____
_____
_____
_____
_____
_____
_____
_____
_____
_____
_____

"Put YOU first."

Before you can help anyone else with their Goals, you must first get your own into shape! Just like being on a plane and they tell you straight.......before helping someone else get the benefit of oxygen make sure you have yours in place first. There are times we have to be a little bit selfish in our priorities, dedication demands it.

My Day /

_____
_____
_____
_____
_____
_____
_____
_____
_____
_____
_____
_____

"Realize your dreams."

We are here but a short while, use every second and value every moment. Do you ever take a step back and imagine what it would be like to achieve the uttermost things that matter to you.....how you would feel, what you would value most? I for one believe if it's worth dreaming, it's worth chasing!

My Day /

_____
_____
_____
_____
_____
_____
_____
_____
_____
_____
_____
_____

"Work the plan."

A plan in itself is not enough, only action will make any dream a reality. We can talk all day, but if we won't put the work in then the dreams are futile. The greatest pleasure of any dream is how YOU came to make it happen, what was it that YOU did to ensure you made it through in the end?

My Day /

_____
_____
_____
_____
_____
_____
_____
_____
_____
_____
_____
_____

"Be the difference."

YOU can be the shining light, you can be the one that makes all the difference, be it in YOUR life and dreams, or in that of another. Think about that, the impact you are a capable of having in any given situation, and work it, show what you've got!

My Day /

_____
_____
_____
_____
_____
_____
_____
_____
_____
_____
_____

"Every minute matters."

As I write this I am using today's downtime to create tomorrow's uptime!
Your story won't write itself..........you have to make the minutes work to make the days matter. Don't let tomorrow be your excuse, get started today.

My Day /

_____
_____
_____
_____
_____
_____
_____
_____
_____
_____
_____
_____

"No holding back."

Once you take that first step then you have started the charge, it's time now to forge ahead with all of your might......face your fears and don't hold back! With each milestone you pass your confidence strengthens, and the big hurdles start to diminish in both size and stature.

My Day /

_____
_____
_____
_____
_____
_____
_____
_____
_____
_____
_____

"Reverse the doubt."

You can quieten the voices going on in your mind, doubting your desires and questioning your inner beliefs. Use that negative energy to your advantage and assure yourself of your own self worth......'why not me, who says I can't come through in first place?'.

My Day /

_____
_____
_____
_____
_____
_____
_____
_____
_____
_____
_____

"You can too."

Watching other people turn their dreams into their reality should serve as motivation not intimidation. You are equally worthy, all they have done is laid out a path, one which you can follow in full or to a point where you feel the urge to branch off and make your own new inroads.

My Day /

_____
_____
_____
_____
_____
_____
_____
_____
_____
_____
_____
_____
_____

"Locate the opening."

Your path is there, between the hedge grow and the trees, you just need to find the right route through. Find the avenue that suits YOU best, the one that makes you most happy, the one that strengthens your resolve and develops you in the way that your journey demands.

My Day /

_____
_____
_____
_____
_____
_____
_____
_____
_____
_____
_____
_____

"Develop your skills."

*Work on your talents, develop your skills,
become better than the competitors coming up.
People may tell you that you have a unique or
special gift but that doesn't mean for you to sit
back and lap it up! Talent in itself will only take
you so far, development through the gears will
be needed if you intend to win the race.*

My Day /

_____
_____
_____
_____
_____
_____
_____
_____
_____
_____
_____
_____

"Learn to win."

That first victory can often be the hardest one to accomplish, that initial feeling that you have made your mark finally. Once you get an appetite for victory, and once you feel that joy, you'll know better how to keep winning and how to build upon it.

My Day /

_____
_____
_____
_____
_____
_____
_____
_____
_____
_____
_____
_____

"Shape your future."

As your journey progresses, and some of your desired opportunities open up, consider your options closely, not every door that opens requires you to go through it. Forge plans for your next steps and choose the route specifically to help you down the road.

My Day /

"Face your fears."

Some of our greatest fears are in fact states of our mind, emotions that are never as deep once we actually face them head on. How often to we delay getting going simply because we have allowed our fear to overcome us, to trap us in a state of paralysis?

My Day /

_____
_____
_____
_____
_____
_____
_____
_____
_____
_____
_____
_____

"Know your strengths."

Get to know yourself deeply, know what your talents are, and better still, learn how to use them to their greatest effect. Too often we feel embarrassed to display our skills, to show off what we have in our locker.....but surely the whole essence of any gift is to understand the benefits of it's use.

My Day /

_____
_____
_____
_____
_____
_____
_____
_____
_____
_____
_____
_____

"Make a commitment."

Make a decision and set a timeframe to go with it......it's at that point only that your dream becomes a tangible Goal. It is the responsibility of you alone to turn that dream into something that can be held, into something that becomes part of your daily reality, into something you will be proud of.

My Day /

_____
_____
_____
_____
_____
_____
_____
_____
_____
_____
_____

"Prepare to succeed."

Are you ready for success, have you considered what it will mean? If you're writing down your Goals and following your plan then why not you. What's to stop you reaching straight for the top, the very peak of the mountain?

My Day /

_____
_____
_____
_____
_____
_____
_____
_____
_____
_____
_____

"Can you lead?"

Have you contemplated leading the show, taking the flock ahead under your direction? Scary thought eh.......but possible, in fact achievable, with just a little flicker of belief. When opportunity knocks be ready to take the baton, be ready to take the lead role.

My Day /

_____
_____
_____
_____
_____
_____
_____
_____
_____
_____
_____

"Learn to love."

Learn to love who you are and you'll find it easier to love others for who they are too. Know who you are and what you stand for, what your quality's are and what your ethics say about you. You are worthy of deep love and there is no better place for it to begin than with the reflection in the mirror.

My Day /

_____
_____
_____
_____
_____
_____
_____
_____
_____
_____
_____
_____

"Invest in YOU."

Put time into your own self development, read, observe, listen........take it all in, and then put your new skills to work for YOU. You cannot seriously expect anyone else to invest in you if you won't first do it for yourself. You must show YOUR level of commitment to the cause, that you too will pour your heart into your own well being.

My Day /

_____
_____
_____
_____
_____
_____
_____
_____
_____
_____
_____
_____

"Decide your future."

Remove the risk of wandering, decide what it is you want, and go out there and grab it with all you can muster. The reason satellite navigation has become standard in almost every car is because in truth, we all prefer to know where we are going.

My Day /

_____
_____
_____
_____
_____
_____
_____
_____
_____
_____
_____
_____

"Love your journey."

If you're loving the journey you are undertaking the bumps in the road will be easier to overcome. Embrace the stresses and strains you will undoubtedly endure, and the successes and joys will mean all the more when they arrive. This is not a 100 meters dash, you're going to have to run for a little bit longer than that.

My Day /

_____

_____

_____

_____

_____

_____

_____

_____

_____

_____

_____

_____

"Produce your best."

Nobody will ever question you for giving your all........never, ever let yourself down with a half baked effort. Of course there are days we will give it our best shot but still come up a little bit short, but that's ok, we can't win every time. But stick to the task in hand, give it another go tomorrow, and your moment of glory shall come.

My Day /

_____
_____
_____
_____
_____
_____
_____
_____
_____
_____
_____
_____

"Fight your corner."

First and foremost you must hold strong your beliefs and stand up for the integrity by which you follow them........don't be swayed with opinions of which carry no value. People will try to steer you off course with their own agendas, it's sad but true, and that is the very point where you must push back those shoulders and raise your chin that little bit higher.

My Day /

_____
_____
_____
_____
_____
_____
_____
_____
_____
_____
_____
_____

"Fulfill your life."

As the clock ticks by know the value of the gift you have been given, use it and appreciate it. Every morning I open my eyes I thank God for the gift of the day, of the joy of another day of opportunity. I am fighting and breathing so in there still stands my chance.

My Day /

_____
_____
_____
_____
_____
_____
_____
_____
_____
_____
_____

"Don't be delayed."

Offer no more excuses, waste not a second........get out there and get the motor running.
Don't cheat yourself with futile excuses, putting off the moment you step out onto the stage and raise your face to the light. This is your time, this is your moment, take it!

My Day /

_____
_____
_____
_____
_____
_____
_____
_____
_____
_____
_____
_____

"Speak with clarity."

When you hold firm a belief know how to express it and be proud of its content. Prepare yourself for the occasion when your chance to speak may well present itself, be ready to vocalize your view, and stand by the principles of your soul.

My Day /

_____
_____
_____
_____
_____
_____
_____
_____
_____
_____
_____
_____

"Take your chance."

You will get opportunities to shine throughout your journey, some when you expect, some not. But whenever they befall you, and if the chance that comes is the one of which you wait, then be ready to grab on with both hands and prove you are worthy of the selectors choice.

My Day /

_____
_____
_____
_____
_____
_____
_____
_____
_____
_____
_____
_____

"Lift your spirit."

Some mornings you actively have to give your mood a lift, you may benefit to visualize one positive thing you can take from your day, and work that thought into your day. Of course there are pressures or worries that can get in our way but we must see them for what they are and realign our focus on what the bigger picture will bring.

My Day /

_____
_____
_____
_____
_____
_____
_____
_____
_____
_____
_____

"Take a risk."

If you don't leave the port you'll never see the ocean, take a chance, what have you got to lose?! It's scary out there, no question, but there is far more risk in not taking your chance than there will ever be if you do. Sometimes you have to learn to swim once your feet hit the water, be ready to start kicking the moment you get in.

My Day /

_____
_____
_____
_____
_____
_____
_____
_____
_____
_____
_____
_____

"Learn to live."

Discover what makes you happy, find the balance that gets the most, and the best, out of you. We hope to find a workplace that makes us happy, and a home to go to the same, but nothing is forever and you are allowed to move your bets. Live life to the best of your ability, we are not here to drown in misery.

My Day /

_____
_____
_____
_____
_____
_____
_____
_____
_____
_____
_____
_____

"Why dream small?"

When we think of dreams we naturally look up, because that's where they'll take us, somewhere that stretches us higher. We have no ambition to be second best or we have no ambition at all. You can be the one on the pedestal, you can win the day.

My Day /

_____
_____
_____
_____
_____
_____
_____
_____
_____
_____
_____
_____

"Work the detail."

Understanding the need for detail, and making use of that additional knowledge, will get us where we're headed an awful lot quicker. We must learn to love the specifics, the finer details and the sharpness that defines us beyond the ordinary.

My Day /

_____
_____
_____
_____
_____
_____
_____
_____
_____
_____
_____

"Why not now."

There is no need to wait for a Monday, or the 1st of the year, to make a new start.........you can make that start right here, right now. We all find the excuses readily......once I've done this, or only after that......but we may just wait until our time has passed and endure days of regret. If you're going to give it a go, why not now, why not throw yourself straight in?

My Day /

_____
_____
_____
_____
_____
_____
_____
_____
_____
_____
_____
_____

"Up the pace."

With that commitment to yourself in place, once you have decided you're setting yourself a time limit and confirm the date.....it's time to really get the ball rolling. Consider your route, those whose help you may require, and get your plan on paper so that you've no excuses to cut the Goal short.

My Day /

_____
_____
_____
_____
_____
_____
_____
_____
_____
_____
_____
_____

"Do you believe?"

Do you really believe in what you are doing, do you really trust in where you are going.......do you believe in the dream you are pursuing? Is it strong enough, has it enough meaning and purpose, will you keep going until the target is met? This is where your commitment shall be tested.

My Day /

_____
_____
_____
_____
_____
_____
_____
_____
_____
_____
_____
_____
_____

"Retain self worth."

Never lower your standards, never bow to morals below your own for a buck, hold your integrity and safeguard your principles. You are who you are because of your own self beliefs, the very make up of your character.......never permit anyone to steal that away from you.

My Day /

_____
_____
_____
_____
_____
_____
_____
_____
_____
_____
_____
_____

"Leave your mark."

In everything we do we leave behind our personal mark, the memory after we've gone of the committed strength of our contribution. Have you considered what yours says about you?

You leave your stamp everywhere you go, make sure it's a mark you can reflect on with pride.

My Day /

_____
_____
_____
_____
_____
_____
_____
_____
_____
_____
_____

"See the future."

Some use meditation others use Goal boards......find what suits you best and visualize what it is you seek most. Get in tune with your Goals and targets, get that you are literally breathing your dream every single day.

My Day /

_____

_____

_____

_____

_____

_____

_____

_____

_____

_____

_____

"Be of value."

The more you have developed your own knowledge and skill set the higher your value shall soar. The more value you bring to a situation the more you will gain from what you can contribute.......remember that when the negotiations begin.

My Day /

_____
_____
_____
_____
_____
_____
_____
_____
_____
_____
_____
_____

"Stop looking back!"

Stop looking in the rear view mirror, it's only for reflection, not for living. We can contemplate but not hibernate, it's time to move on. Your history has been set but your future has not, focus on where you are headed, you already know where you have been.

My Day /

_____
_____
_____
_____
_____
_____
_____
_____
_____
_____
_____

"Sometimes it's tough."

Strength shall come from your toughest challenges, along with the knowledge and experience these tests shall bring. Some moments will be testing, some very low points possibly, but you're only passing through, this is not the final destination.

My Day /

_____
_____
_____
_____
_____
_____
_____
_____
_____
_____
_____

"Do not overthink."

Think out your plans and routes you are intending to travel, give them the proper analysis they will merit and then.......get to work. Some of it we will pick up along the way, we cannot afford to overthink any situation or we will end up doing nothing.

My Day /

_____
_____
_____
_____
_____
_____
_____
_____
_____
_____
_____

"Do something productive."

There are times our focus can shift to money or the material joys it brings but never lose sight of the purpose of your works, do not lose sight of the depth of your dream. When the opportunity to create something special presents itself it would be wasteful to miss our chance.

My Day /

_____
_____
_____
_____
_____
_____
_____
_____
_____
_____
_____

"Ask for help."

Don't be frightened to seek out those who have greater knowledge or skills than ours, that's how we learn. And don't be afraid to ASK them their opinions or viewpoints.......they've been there too and know how tough it can be.

My Day /

_____

_____

_____

_____

_____

_____

_____

_____

_____

_____

_____

"Tackle the challenges."

Don't sidestep the tests.......rethink the route or replan the direction, but don't bury your head in the sand, it won't go away if you don't take it on some way. Challenges are the making of us, sometimes they teach us just what we need to know.

My Day /

_____
_____
_____
_____
_____
_____
_____
_____
_____
_____
_____

"Never give up."

There's always a way, please don't give up or become consumed with fear or doubt, nothing is ever insurmountable, the fight is not lost. Do you need support, is there someone who can help you overcome this block in the road? Or do you need simply to reset your plan and try another path? Take a moment, work it through, you are still on track.

My Day /

_____
_____
_____
_____
_____
_____
_____
_____
_____
_____
_____
_____

"Just another step......."

Sometimes it only requires one more push to make the breakthrough. Go on, you may be closer than you think. Isn't it amazing the number of times we've heard people tell their personal stories and recount, just at the point they were ready to throw in the towel.........boom, the door broke free!

My Day /

_____
_____
_____
_____
_____
_____
_____
_____
_____
_____
_____
_____

"It's happening now."

This is your time, their is no dress rehearsal, we are now at the point where you have to show up. Are you ready, have you prepared the best you can for this very moment........are you ready to shout out at the top of your voice? Then GO!

My Day /

_____
_____
_____
_____
_____
_____
_____
_____
_____
_____
_____

"Believe in yourself."

Of course doubts will come, questions or seeds of personal lacking.......but YOU ARE good enough, you are able enough to see the way through. The only way you are ever going to know if you can make it is if you now push on to that next big step.

My Day /

_____
_____
_____
_____
_____
_____
_____
_____
_____
_____
_____

"Never stop trying."

You can make your own luck, you can force the openings to present themselves.......out work the competition and never stop trying. The waysiders will drop off along the way, but YOU won't, you can't, you have got this and it's now within your grasp.

My Day /

_____
_____
_____
_____
_____
_____
_____
_____
_____
_____
_____
_____

"You can deliver."

You have enough in your armory, you have the talent and the strength, you just need now add the ACTION. Show up, stand up, let the World see what you've got, it is now your time, time to deliver.

My Day /

_____
_____
_____
_____
_____
_____
_____
_____
_____
_____
_____
_____

"Today is yours."

If your eyes opened this morning, and you've taken an easy breathe, then the day is yours to make something special of. Value every second, value another day to give it a go......to build on where you are at, and move another step closer on your passageway of growth.

My Day /

_____
_____
_____
_____
_____
_____
_____
_____
_____
_____
_____
_____

"Be the one."

It's hard to imagine how others view us, to let your guard down and step into the limelight. But you can, and the time will come when to some extent, you must........to grab that chance.
You can be the one to add the final ingredient, you can be the one who brings it all together.

My Day /

_____
_____
_____
_____
_____
_____
_____
_____
_____
_____
_____

"One special moment."

It may only take that one one special moment for what YOU do to be recognized, for YOUR breakthrough to come. It only takes the right person, in the right moment, and you are there! It will come, be persistent, keep on trying, a split second will make all the difference.

My Day /

_____
_____
_____
_____
_____
_____
_____
_____
_____
_____
_____

"Do it differently."

What is it about you that makes you stand out, what is YOUR point of difference? We all have it, that unique little trait that others don't, that special little shine that people remind us they see! Find it, harness it, and use it.

My Day /

_____
_____
_____
_____
_____
_____
_____
_____
_____
_____
_____
_____

"Always show up."

People have an expectation of us and that can add pressure... but also excitement, an excitement that, if we use it correctly, will drive us through!
Never let yourself down by being there only in presence, if you're going to show up at all, make it a performance to be remembered.

My Day /

_____
_____
_____
_____
_____
_____
_____
_____
_____
_____
_____

"You are irreplaceable."

There is no one quite like you, there is no one there to take your place........you are you like no other could be. And again, it can be difficult for us to grasp what we mean to others, to our family, our friends and our colleagues, but believe me, you are irreplaceable in each of their eyes.

My Day /

_____
_____
_____
_____
_____
_____
_____
_____
_____
_____
_____

"Deliver upon request."

When your chance comes now are you ready to step up, can you put on the kit and take your place in the team? When that time comes, the opportunity you've been crying out for presents itself, be sure you ARE going to jump at it with your very best shot.

My Day /

_____
_____
_____
_____
_____
_____
_____
_____
_____
_____
_____

"Don't let up."

When the chips are down and you're feeling low, you may need to dig as deep as you can and rekindle the fighting spirit to get you moving forward again. The race has some miles still to pass, it's not yet time for rest, we must find the inner strength to continue the journey.

My Day /

_____
_____
_____
_____
_____
_____
_____
_____
_____
_____
_____

"Get back up."

Dust yourself down, clean off the grazes, and be ready to fight on.
Don't be overcome by the weight of the battle, reassess what has gone wrong........and get ready to give yourself another go!

My Day/

_____
_____
_____
_____
_____
_____
_____
_____
_____
_____
_____

"Overcome the odds."

Don't be put off because the odds are against you, everyone loves an underdog remember. And sometimes that fighting spirit you have learned and developed over the years can be the additional factor when it comes to the head to heads.

My Day /

_____
_____
_____
_____
_____
_____
_____
_____
_____
_____
_____

"Stand up strong."

Chin up, shoulders back..........and let's see what you've got. No hesitation, no second guessing, give it your best shot. You have nothing to lose and everything to gain, we're here for the long game, this is only another step.

My Day /

_____

_____

_____

_____

_____

_____

_____

_____

_____

_____

_____

"Don't be afraid."

Of course we have fears, rumblings of butterfly's in the stomach.......but use that as your motivator, as the emotion that drives you on. Don't let it restrict the clarity of your actions, don't let fear get in the way of your success.

My Day /

_____
_____
_____
_____
_____
_____
_____
_____
_____
_____
_____

"Understand the difference."

What will it mean to me if I achieve my goals, what will it mean to those closest to me.......and who will I become along the way? Find the answers to these questions and you'll understand the purpose and reason for your Goals. This is YOUR Goal remember, this is about what it makes of YOU.

My Day /

_____

_____

_____

_____

_____

_____

_____

_____

_____

_____

_____

"Where am I?"

Where do I currently stand, do I know......how far into my journey am I......am I making the progress I yearn and am I doing it at the pace I'd set? Ask someone to set a Goal and a date and they'll overshoot on one and underestimate on the other, be fair to yourself but don't let up.

My Day /

_____

_____

_____

_____

_____

_____

_____

_____

_____

_____

_____

_____

"Adjust your settings."

Have you ever looked at what you are doing and thought simply.....'this isn't working, I'm not getting there this way'? If what you're doing isn't giving you the results you desire then change something........your thinking, your direction, your actions.

My Day /

_____
_____
_____
_____
_____
_____
_____
_____
_____
_____
_____
_____

"Remind yourself WHY!"

Why are you doing what you are doing, why did you set out to achieve this Goal, where lies your reason and purpose.......? Ask yourself this......why did I challenge myself in the first place, what was the object of my desires, what got me started and where lies the end?

My Day /

_____
_____
_____
_____
_____
_____
_____
_____
_____
_____
_____
_____

"Do your best."

If your efforts were up for review by one of your peers how much harder would you work to impress? And so why not put that amount of effort in to impress yourself more.........after all you're not doing it for them, you're doing it for you!

My Day /

_____
_____
_____
_____
_____
_____
_____
_____
_____
_____
_____

"Speak doesn't count."

Action is what matters most........only say it if you are going to do it. The greatest action is to underpromise and to over deliver, never the other way around!

My Day /

_____

_____

_____

_____

_____

_____

_____

_____

_____

_____

"Travel with Time."

Keep up to date with what's going on around you, use it.......don't lag behind, keep moving forward. If technological knowledge is required, get it, if practical skills are required, get them. Don't be found wanting through lack of personal input, be first in line very time!

My Day /

_____

_____

_____

_____

_____

_____

_____

_____

_____

_____

_____

"Count your blessings."

Do you value and appreciate who you have and what you have in life, as little as it sometimes can feel it's often a lot more than many others can count on. If you can, begin every day with gratitude, it does not get much healthier a place to start than that!

My Day /

_____
_____
_____
_____
_____
_____
_____
_____
_____
_____
_____
_____

"Best foot forward."

Your best each day will vary, depending on how you're feeling, but be sure it's your best for that day........all you've got, the best you can manage.
And people will get it, they'll be understanding when they know you're one who gives their all.

My Day /

_____
_____
_____
_____
_____
_____
_____
_____
_____
_____
_____
_____

"Trust your instincts."

If something doesn't feel right it is your subconscious telling you to steer clear.......learn to trust that feeling, it's rarely wrong. In the words of Sir Alex Ferguson...."If there is any doubt, there is no doubt."

My Day /

_____
_____
_____
_____
_____
_____
_____
_____
_____
_____
_____

"Be a student."

Be teachable, allow yourself to learn new things, regardless of time, regardless of age. I've found it one of the most frustrating things in life, when I see talent in someone, but I also see arrogance, arrogance that prevents learning which prevents growth.

MyDay /

"Be a teacher."

Be prepared to share what you know, have the courage to pass on the knowledge you have gained. Wisdom is only wasted if it is not passed down the line. Make someone's day a little lighter, help them along their way.

My Day /

_____
_____
_____
_____
_____
_____
_____
_____
_____
_____
_____
_____

"Love yourself FIRST."

Before you can help another you must first learn to love yourself and to invest in your own well being........take time out to remind yourself what makes YOU happy.

My Day /

_____
_____
_____
_____
_____
_____
_____
_____
_____
_____
_____
_____

"Build deep foundations."

The stronger the foundations the more resilient the building, and the better prepared you'll be when the wind batters the walls.

My Day /

_____
_____
_____
_____
_____
_____
_____
_____
_____
_____
_____

"Drive your passions."

If you don't drive what you are most passionate about who will?! Follow your dreams with no excuses, go get what your heart desires. This is your dream remember, no one else's.

My Day /

_____

_____

_____

_____

_____

_____

_____

_____

_____

_____

_____

"Increase the volume."

If no one is hearing you turn up the volume, work a little harder, shout a little louder.......do not go unnoticed. If you want to be seen you may have to make a little more noise.

My Day /

_____
_____
_____
_____
_____
_____
_____
_____
_____
_____
_____
_____

"Throw another ball."

Just when you're ready to give up, consider this......what if you're very next throw was the one that hit the mark............what if the very next ball was the one that saw you through? Goals and ambitions are not your job, there is no quitting, there is only you, and your desire and will to achieve your dreams. Keep going till the line has been crossed.

My Day /

_____
_____
_____
_____
_____
_____
_____
_____
_____
_____
_____
_____

"Cultivate good thinking."

Start the day with one good thought and allow it to develop a positive state of mind for the day. If negativity enters consider a positive action to turn it around, and take THAT action. How we approach a situation can depend greatly upon our mood, so we have to learn to react to our mood and adjust it to our advantage when needs must.

My Day /

_____
_____
_____
_____
_____
_____
_____
_____
_____
_____
_____
_____

"Improve your talent."

It's not enough to accept you have a talent or a gift, the goal is to see what you can turn it in to.....a hobby or a way of life. Don't rest on your laurels, the experience will be of value.

My Day /

_____
_____
_____
_____
_____
_____
_____
_____
_____
_____
_____

"Control your reaction."

If you can't control your reaction you will become emotionally distracted in situations where your mind must be clear to ensure a safe pathway through. Take a deep breath, or even a night's sleep, before confirming your response.

My Day /

_____
_____
_____
_____
_____
_____
_____
_____
_____
_____
_____
_____

"Unlock your thinking."

Old thinking won't provide solutions to new problems. You will have to assess each part of the process in the new way it will present itself, take the necessary steps to adjust your thinking, and your answers will be better served.

My Day /

_____
_____
_____
_____
_____
_____
_____
_____
_____
_____
_____
_____

"Listen to learn."

God gifted you with TWO ears and ONE mouth for a reason.......listen twice as much as you talk. And listen acutely, not passively.......the nodding dog process where you are not tuned in but simply serving up a smile just won't cut it. Any chance to learn should be appreciated in its own merit.

My Day /

_____
_____
_____
_____
_____
_____
_____
_____
_____
_____
_____

"Avoid the sheep."

Don't get lost in the crowd, trust your vision and follow your dreams. We can easily be caught up in the movement, sailing along and letting time slip away, passive progress. Be different, set new marks, live as you choose to live.

My Day /

_____
_____
_____
_____
_____
_____
_____
_____
_____
_____
_____
_____

"Know your team."

Know who's on your side, know who is not, and understand the difference. Knowing your allies AND your enemies will save you much wasted time and heartache, as some will pretend to be one, whilst being the other.

My Day /

_____
_____
_____
_____
_____
_____
_____
_____
_____
_____
_____

"Preparation is key."

Getting yourself properly prepared will ensure you, in some way, can deal with most eventualities that will come your way, that you are ready when opportunity knocks. Don't wing it, know your stuff!

My Day /

_____
_____
_____
_____
_____
_____
_____
_____
_____
_____

"Success is obsessive."

Once you taste success, once you make that initial breakthrough, your hunger and desire to feel it again will overcome you, guiding you in the art of winning. Once is not enough, you are capable of way more.

My Day /

_____
_____
_____
_____
_____
_____
_____
_____
_____
_____
_____

"Understand your field."

Discover the 'how to's' and the 'who can's' of your game, find out what you don't know already and discover better what you believe you already do. In any walk of life people make an enormous difference, find out who will be key to your progress.

My Day /

_____
_____
_____
_____
_____
_____
_____
_____
_____
_____
_____

"Cultivate your crops."

Grow, grow and grow what you have and who you are. Be relentless, don't stand still and don't accept that you have made it........this is a journey of fulfillment and with infinite opportunity. Our journey is what will stand us in stead, not just the medals at the finish.

My Day /

_____
_____
_____
_____
_____
_____
_____
_____
_____
_____
_____
_____

"Visualize the win."

Imagine yourself at the top of the tree, see yourself as the victor, see yourself already achieving the Goal you so desperately desire. And with it you must envisage what it will give you, tangible Goals with tangible outcomes.

My Day /

_____

_____

_____

_____

_____

_____

_____

_____

_____

_____

_____

"Open your eyes."

There lies opportunity around us every day, opportunity to discover a new way or to introduce a new product or viewpoint. Seek out the opening and you'll discover new adventures. Learn something you've never known!

My Day /

_____
_____
_____
_____
_____
_____
_____
_____
_____
_____
_____

"Share your vision."

At first be selective of who may be on your side, but once you are sure, involve your closest in what you see, gain their support. It can be invaluable to have people on board who can lift you when you need it most, and crucially the people who are committed also to your success.

My Day /

_____
_____
_____
_____
_____
_____
_____
_____
_____
_____
_____

"See it through."

Unless something will cause you personal harm do not quit on unfinished business, see it through to a conclusion.......there's no point involving yourself in a story if you don't discover how it ends.

My Day /

_____
_____
_____
_____
_____
_____
_____
_____
_____
_____
_____
_____

"Commit to excellence."

Be it in standards or effort, be sure that you are offering your very best as frequently as possible, no half hearted presentations, no lackadaisical moments.

My Day /

_____
_____
_____
_____
_____
_____
_____
_____
_____
_____
_____
_____

"Mountains or Molehills."

Mountains are often created in our minds, but when we actually face these challenges they turn out to be molehills in reality. Face them head on and early, don't delay, don't waste time pondering.

My Day /

_____
_____
_____
_____
_____
_____
_____
_____
_____
_____
_____

"Talent won't suffice."

Talent, in itself, is not enough.......it requires the addition of hard work, determination and perseverance before it will bring you the rewards that it truly merits.

My Day /

_____
_____
_____
_____
_____
_____
_____
_____
_____
_____
_____

"Practice makes permanent."

Whatever you practice on a regular basis you will perfect but what if you are practicing in the wrong way? Practicing something repeatedly will ensure it's permanence so be sure to be getting your training methods right!

My Day /

_____
_____
_____
_____
_____
_____
_____
_____
_____
_____
_____
_____

"Fight the doubt."

Every day we face the challenge of doubt, that little voice that chirps away at us, telling us it won't happen, it won't work......to hell with that voice, your are capable and it IS possible.

My Day /

_____
_____
_____
_____
_____
_____
_____
_____
_____
_____
_____

"Acquire the skills."

We will need the skill set to succeed, we will need to learn the tricks of the trade, the foundations of our structure. And so when your mouth opens you must know the facts!

My Day /

_____
_____
_____
_____
_____
_____
_____
_____
_____
_____
_____

"Value the moment.'

Our Goals exist in the future but we must remember to live in the now. Don't wish your days away, work towards your Goals of course, but spent each day living and working the plan......these are the best days, value the special moments.

My Day /

_____
_____
_____
_____
_____
_____
_____
_____
_____
_____
_____

"Carry the Torch."

When things aren't going so great, when those around you are in low spirits, can YOU be the one to carry them through, can you be the one to take up the torch and lead from the front? Sometimes even for short bursts, but it makes a world of difference when someone knows you are there as a shoulder to lean on.

My Day /

_____
_____
_____
_____
_____
_____
_____
_____
_____
_____
_____

"Deliver the goods."

When the chance opens up, and your moment arrives........make sure you are ready to go in to the battle and win the day. You have been chasing this for some time, and undoubtedly your chance will come, so be prepared, be ready to jump.

My Day /

_____
_____
_____
_____
_____
_____
_____
_____
_____
_____
_____
_____

"Understand the reason."

It is crucial to have an understanding of why you are doing it, especially when the chips are down, here you'll find all the more reason to come out fighting and last the pace.

My Day /

_____

_____

_____

_____

_____

_____

_____

_____

_____

_____

_____

_____

"Create positive images."

Visualize what you dream of, not what you fear.......this is essential to your success! Make a visual list of what you wish to attract and focus purely upon THAT.

My Day /

_____
_____
_____
_____
_____
_____
_____
_____
_____
_____
_____
_____

"Success isn't accidental."

Know this, and grasp it wholeheartedly, it WILL NOT happen by itself.......YOU are the driver of this bus, and you are the one that will determine the destination.

My Day /

_____
_____
_____
_____
_____
_____
_____
_____
_____
_____
_____

"Direct your passion."

What grabs hold of you, what excites you the most, and have you yet worked out how best to direct that enthusiasm? Your passion becomes your dream and your dream becomes your reality......IF you focus and direct it exactly where you want it to go.

My Day /

_____
_____
_____
_____
_____
_____
_____
_____
_____
_____
_____
_____
_____

"Do not settle."

Your time is limited, your window of opportunity doesn't last forever. Please don't let it slip past whilst you 'settle' for an easy life. Go in search of what you can become, go find the person you can grow into.

My Day /

_____
_____
_____
_____
_____
_____
_____
_____
_____
_____
_____
_____

"Design your future."

See it, feel it, materialize it!
Figure out what you want, what it looks like in specific images, then spend every day constructing your life in just the way you want it.

My Day /

_____
_____
_____
_____
_____
_____
_____
_____
_____
_____
_____

"Channel your thinking."

Focus on what you're chasing, align your thinking on your target and remind yourself every day what your reasoning behind it all is. You have this chance to go be the person of your dreams, do not brush past it, don't let YOU miss out.

My Day /

_____
_____
_____
_____
_____
_____
_____
_____
_____
_____
_____

"What's your story?"

Who are you, where are you headed, what is your point?
Before finding anyone else, go on a journey of self discovery......find out about YOU first and create your very own story to tell.

My Day /

_____
_____
_____
_____
_____
_____
_____
_____
_____
_____
_____
_____

"Stay on track."

You'd be foolish to think you won't derail from time to time, dragged off in other tangents and time wasting exercises. But remember it's all part of the learning, part of your experience......so be sure to get yourself back on track ASAP!

My Day /

_____
_____
_____
_____
_____
_____
_____
_____
_____
_____
_____
_____

"Visualization changes outcomes."

The outcome you visualize, good AND bad, is the outcome you will attract. You wouldn't go the cinema to watch a rubbish story now would you......go for an Oscar winning performance.

My Day /

_____
_____
_____
_____
_____
_____
_____
_____
_____
_____
_____

"See your journey."

Can you see it, stretched out in front of you, the joys, the smiles, the challenges and the rewards? it's YOU, it's all there for YOU, it's all part of your journey if you so decide it to be.

My Day /

_____
_____
_____
_____
_____
_____
_____
_____
_____
_____
_____

"Move yourself forward."

What will it take to get you to take that first step, what will see you take that 'leap of faith'? Will you unlock the key and open the door of your fullest potential, will you walk down the path of fulfillment?

My Day /

_____

_____
_____
_____
_____
_____
_____
_____
_____
_____
_____

"Defy the odds."

Where you begin your journey matters way less than where you end it. Don't play the blame game, do yourself justice and reach your ultimate Goals. You can be the first in your line to reach new levels of achievement.

My Day /

_____
_____
_____
_____
_____
_____
_____
_____
_____
_____
_____
_____

"Look straight ahead."

It's easy to get bogged down in what has gone before and how it has affected you, or even what is going on around you. Remember though, there is only one direction you're headed and that lies straight out in front. Apply your focus where you're headed, not where you've been......the difference will have consequences.

My Day /

_____
_____
_____
_____
_____
_____
_____
_____
_____
_____
_____
_____

"Lengthen your stride."

Just as your competitors start gaining on you, or when you are slipping back into your comfort zone, stretch your legs a little and push on to avoid old habits catching you up. We must maintain a steady pace, keeping out in front and keeping the field just that little bit in our wake.

My Day /

_____
_____
_____
_____
_____
_____
_____
_____
_____
_____
_____

"See the opportunity."

Opportunities present themselves often enough, but you will only recognize them if your receptors are switched on. Keep both your eyes and ears open at all times, you'll pick up on your chances that way and nothing will pass you by.

My Day /

_____
_____
_____
_____
_____
_____
_____
_____
_____
_____
_____
_____

"Open the gate."

Often our chance appears but we don't have the boldness to push our way through, so don't be afraid to take firm hold of that gate and thrust it wide open.

My Day /

_____
_____
_____
_____
_____
_____
_____
_____
_____
_____
_____

"Steer your vessel."

If you are going to control the route of your journey then you must steer your way through the mire. Storms will come but they also will pass, keep your eye on the final dock and you'll get there soon enough.

My Day /

_____
_____
_____
_____
_____
_____
_____
_____
_____
_____
_____

"Enjoy the trip."

Regardless of how many times I win or lose at the table, I always try to hold dear something I've gained from each experience, something I know that can help me on my way.

My Day /

_____
_____
_____
_____
_____
_____
_____
_____
_____
_____
_____

"You have time."

Too often our excuse is that we don't have the time or it's too late for us, but that is not the case, the time will pass anyway, how you use it is what will make the difference.

My Day /

_____
_____
_____
_____
_____
_____
_____
_____
_____
_____
_____

"Pitch yourself high."

Nobody dreams of being 5th or 6th in line, our ultimate dream is to be No1.......so don't pitch yourself too low, be prepared to take 1st place.

My Day /

_____
_____
_____
_____
_____
_____
_____
_____
_____
_____
_____
_____

"Doubt brings fear."

If you allow doubt to linger in your mind without taking positive, responsive action it can paralyze you, stopping you before you even leave the blocks!

My Day /

_____
_____
_____
_____
_____
_____
_____
_____
_____
_____
_____

"You're your chance."

YOU are your best chance, you are the one that carries your own torch, the buck stops with you. So understand the difference you can make in all of it.......it ALL begins and ends with YOU.

My Day /

_____
_____
_____
_____
_____
_____
_____
_____
_____
_____
_____

"Control the pace."

There are times you will have to speed things up, a needed thrust of energy to get the job done. But also there are times to slow things down, showing patience and being meticulous in your detail.

My Day /

_____
_____
_____
_____
_____
_____
_____
_____
_____
_____
_____

"Consider other opinions."

Do not get railroaded into singular thinking, do not close your mind to alternative viewpoints. Try to see things from the opposite angle and consider ALL the options available to you.

My Day /

_____
_____
_____
_____
_____
_____
_____
_____
_____
_____
_____

"Don't react emotionally."

Once you react emotionally you show your hand, you lose control and will often cost you the fight. If you can, remove yourself from the situation and give yourself a moment before you go again or voice your opinion.

My Day /

_____
_____
_____
_____
_____
_____
_____
_____
_____
_____
_____
_____

"Understand the benefits."

Before committing to a situation or opportunity, consider the positives......and the negatives. Not every chance you get is a chance worth taking. Weigh it all up before diving in, be sure there is a benefit to be had from getting yourself involved.

My Day /

_____
_____
_____
_____
_____
_____
_____
_____
_____
_____
_____

"Stop in time."

Some things won't work out, sometimes damage limitation is called for, know when to keep going but always know when it's time to try another path.

My Day /

_____
_____
_____
_____
_____
_____
_____
_____
_____
_____
_____
_____

"Evaluate your position."

Remember to take regular evaluation points to see if you're headed in the right direction, and to check you haven't strayed from the path too far.

My Day /

_____
_____
_____
_____
_____
_____
_____
_____
_____
_____
_____
_____

"Believe you can."

As much as 90% of what we think about daily is negative, can you imagine the change to your results if you showed a little belief in yourself? Can you imagine the outcomes if you applied 90% positive thinking to your day?!

My Day /

_____
_____
_____
_____
_____
_____
_____
_____
_____
_____
_____
_____

"Give your all."

No point in showing up half prepared, no point in giving half of what you can, half of the person you truly are........if you're going to display your character, make sure to not let yourself down. Make sure what you leave in others memory of you justifies what you have to offer.

My Day /

_____
_____
_____
_____
_____
_____
_____
_____
_____
_____
_____
_____

"Develop personal strategies."

Work out your plan of action, consider your best routes forward, who can help you.....and how you can bring all this together to assist you in your journey. Work out your plan, then work your plan!

My Day /

_____

_____

_____

_____

_____

_____

_____

_____

_____

_____

_____

"Define your time."

While we have the joy of being here on this planet, what manner with which shall we leave our stamp upon it, what everlasting memory shall we leave behind.......how shall WE define our time here?

My Day /

_____
_____
_____
_____
_____
_____
_____
_____
_____
_____
_____

"Retain personal thanks."

Regardless of what's going on, or where we are in the process of our journey, we must always stop and take stock of the people and things we currently have in our life.......always have thanks, always retain appreciation.

My Day /

_____
_____
_____
_____
_____
_____
_____
_____
_____
_____
_____
_____

"Review your day."

It is crucial to check your score, to review the results good and bad, and to fully consider the path ahead for the following day. Find the time, find a peaceful place if you can, and properly consider how happy you are with your days results.

My Day /

_____
_____
_____
_____
_____
_____
_____
_____
_____
_____
_____

"Go another round."

Have you ever left a situation only to wonder later, "what if I'd just given it one more go....?" Whilst the fight is still in you do you have the courage to get back up and go just one more round!

My Day /

_____
_____
_____
_____
_____
_____
_____
_____
_____
_____
_____

"Always retain hope."

We face many challenging events in our life, tests that sometimes seem to get the better of us, but so long as we can retain hope we will always stand a chance.

My Day /

_____
_____
_____
_____
_____
_____
_____
_____
_____
_____
_____
_____

"What motivates you?

What thrusts you out the door in the morning, what excites you most and are you actively working towards it? How long does it keep your motivation going, does it need a little boost from time to time, are you actively refueling your enthusiasm for the cause you have selected?

My Day /

_____
_____
_____
_____
_____
_____
_____
_____
_____
_____
_____

"Consider the upsides?"

Can you imagine what it would mean if you achieve your dreams, what it would mean not only to you, but to those around you too? And how you would feel with the joy of success, how will you feel when you embrace that lap of honor?

My Day /

_____
_____
_____
_____
_____
_____
_____
_____
_____
_____
_____

"Earn your seat."

To gain the respect of your peers and role models you must first earn the right, displaying the qualities and endeavor that no doubt took them their first. Outwork those around you, prove you are worthy of selection.

My Day /

_____
_____
_____
_____
_____
_____
_____
_____
_____
_____
_____
_____

"Develop a reputation."

Become a reliable soul, someone who can be trusted and someone of value. Show up on time, take pride in your appearance, work harder than all others.......it'll be noticed, believe me, it'll be noticed.

My Day /

_____

_____

_____

_____

_____

_____

_____

_____

_____

_____

_____

_____

"Hear good advice."

We can get so caught up in our journey we forget to hear what is going on around us, occasionally missing out on good advice available from those who have already been over the course.

My Day /

_____
_____
_____
_____
_____
_____
_____
_____
_____
_____
_____
_____

"Display self belief."

If you can't show a belief in your dream then for sure no one else will. Have conviction in your voice and in your behavior, show them you are the real deal and they'll sit up and listen.

My Day /

_____
_____
_____
_____
_____
_____
_____
_____
_____
_____
_____
_____

"Eradicate self doubt."

There are of course days of doubt, we don't feel at our best, the energy has dipped.....
But that's when the Goal is paramount, a focus to lift you, the reason to continue.

My Day /

_____
_____
_____
_____
_____
_____
_____
_____
_____
_____
_____

"Lose the ego."

This isn't about showing off or looking cool, this is about achieving something special, about doing something significant with your life.

My Day /

_____
_____
_____
_____
_____
_____
_____
_____
_____
_____
_____

"Release the past."

It's gone, those bumps in the road, the skin off your knees.......they come and they go.
Don't look back without learning, and then leave it be, you don't have the time.

My Day /

_____
_____
_____
_____
_____
_____
_____
_____
_____
_____
_____

"Storms don't last."

Regardless of how deep in you get, of how low you may be feeling, give yourself a break....it will not last, your breakthrough is not far off.

My Day /

_____
_____
_____
_____
_____
_____
_____
_____
_____
_____
_____
_____

"Shoot the ball."

There comes a point in life where YOU have to take the chance if you are to become the main striker. You have to discover that deeper desire, the courage inside of you, and to release that power with every ounce of strength you have in you.

My Day /

_____
_____
_____
_____
_____
_____
_____
_____
_____
_____
_____
_____

"Work your strengths."

Whatever you have to offer, make sure you do so in abundance, make sure you don't leave any gas in the tank, give them all you've got.......and no regrets for later. Your strengths are yours alone, use them, trust them, let them be your difference.

My Day /

_____
_____
_____
_____
_____
_____
_____
_____
_____
_____
_____

"Walk the coals."

Be prepared to get your hands dirty, walk the trenches to learn the guts of your craft, the heart of your chosen passion. Experiences gained you will carry with you forever, experiences that will take you over the coals and further beyond.

My Day /

_____
_____
_____
_____
_____
_____
_____
_____
_____
_____
_____

"Go with intent."

Walk with confidence, inner belief and a deliberate display of what you have to offer. Don't confuse with arrogance remember, self confidence and ego are not the same message and most people can spot the difference.

My Day /

_____
_____
_____
_____
_____
_____
_____
_____
_____
_____
_____
_____

"I'm in charge."

Don't get caught up in the blame game, your choices create your paths, you are accountable, review your decisions. Failure is ok but learn from it, there lies the root of your success, all under your own control.

My Day /

_____
_____
_____
_____
_____
_____
_____
_____
_____
_____
_____

"You are key."

How you behave, how you react, what you display about yourself to others will show how vital you are in the equation.......give people reason to buy into you, cement their decision that YOU are the one to select.

My Day /

_____
_____
_____
_____
_____
_____
_____
_____
_____
_____
_____

"Open the door."

If that door shows the slightest bit of light shining through, kick it open, drive your opportunity and get in there. Some of the best chances in life come when we least expect them so have your ears and eyes open and be ready to grab it with both hands.

My Day /

_____
_____
_____
_____
_____
_____
_____
_____
_____
_____
_____

"Outwork all others."

Be it smarter or harder, you must display a passion that is unlike no other, you must be the one who others try to keep up with, you can set the pace. You are the one in control of your own destiny.

My Day /

_____
_____
_____
_____
_____
_____
_____
_____
_____
_____
_____
_____

"Intensity produces results."

High intensity produces the best results, be it in sport or in life, the person who pushes and presses the most is the one that rules the game.

My Day /

_____
_____
_____
_____
_____
_____
_____
_____
_____
_____
_____

"Embody your worth."

Never allow anyone the opportunity to undermine your value, only you can do that, and you're not going to........you know your own value, use it!

My Day /

_____
_____
_____
_____
_____
_____
_____
_____
_____
_____
_____
_____

"Search your soul."

How much do you want it.......really, how deep within yourself are you prepared to search for the ultimate answer? You are capable of growth, you are capable of greater things......find it, and use it.

My Day /

_____
_____
_____
_____
_____
_____
_____
_____
_____
_____
_____

"Show your diversity."

Be adaptable, be available to change, to new learning and new areas of growth. The ones who can be most capable of adjusting to new ideas and new platforms, will be the ones who last the test of time.

My Day /

_____
_____
_____
_____
_____
_____
_____
_____
_____
_____
_____
_____

"Are you progressing?"

You have to know if you're making progress.....or not! Are you on the right path or is it time for an adjustment? Don't wander, don't waste your time. Keep track of your progress and you'll keep moving forward.

My Day /

_____
_____
_____
_____
_____
_____
_____
_____
_____
_____
_____
_____

"Make a difference."

If you can be the shining light and the one to create betterment then be it, you never know what it may mean to someone in need. You just never know the difference you can make.

My Day /

_____
_____
_____
_____
_____
_____
_____
_____
_____
_____
_____
_____

"Learn to fight."

There are times it's going to feel really tough, challenges we'd all rather avoid.......but in these most testing of times how hard will you fight? How deep is your resolve, how much do you want to taste the victory?

My Day /

_____
_____
_____
_____
_____
_____
_____
_____
_____
_____
_____
_____

"Stand up straight."

Keep your chin up high, look others in the eye, be proud that you are who you are and that you are on your way. You have everything to stand proud for, you have everything to gain.......this is your time.

My Day /

_____
_____
_____
_____
_____
_____
_____
_____
_____
_____
_____
_____

"Measure the risk."

Risk cuts both ways, the risk if you do, the risk if you don't..........weigh up the impact of either (to you) and where it'll leave you at each stage of your journey.

My Day /

_____
_____
_____
_____
_____
_____
_____
_____
_____
_____
_____
_____

"The reward is......."

For YOU to decide, what is your goal, what does your dream look like, where does the finishing line come into sight for YOU?

My Day /

_____
_____
_____
_____
_____
_____
_____
_____
_____
_____
_____
_____

"Embrace the challenge."

We all have a reason for the odds to be against us, but so what.......where we are going is all that matters, and where we start from.....well that is what it is, and we won't allow it to hold us back.

My Day /

_____
_____
_____
_____
_____
_____
_____
_____
_____
_____
_____

"Throw another punch."

As a boxing fan I've seen this many times......just when a fighter looked like he was dead on his feet, he throws that one more punch that crowns him the Champ, it can be all it takes to make that breakthrough.

My Day /

_____
_____
_____
_____
_____
_____
_____
_____
_____
_____
_____

"Answer to you."

The person who's approval should be first and foremost in your mind is YOURS! You are leading the path here, you are the one who's opinion matters the most and you are the one who the responsibility ends with.

My Day /

_____
_____
_____
_____
_____
_____
_____
_____
_____
_____
_____

"Force or Reason."

Are you the type who has to be forced to do what doesn't suit you, or can you be reasoned with to see the benefits of doing the tasks you don't like? One question.........who benefits most from YOU doing the right thing?

My Day /

_____
_____
_____
_____
_____
_____
_____
_____
_____
_____
_____
_____

"Use the pain."

When you are hurting, when you are suffering the grazes of a fall, it will reflect you at your weakest or your strongest.........use it to your advantage, come out fighting.

My Day /

_____
_____
_____
_____
_____
_____
_____
_____
_____
_____
_____

"Create your trigger."

Have something that triggers good feeling, the thing that lifts you when you need it most...Music, an image, a goal chart.......yours, your call, your trigger moment.

My Day /

_____
_____
_____
_____
_____
_____
_____
_____
_____
_____
_____

"Prepare your pitch."

How shall you appear, what are you going to say, how is the flow going to run......
Be ready prepared, know what you are there to deliver, do not let your personal standards down.

My Day /

_____
_____
_____
_____
_____
_____
_____
_____
_____
_____
_____
_____

"Project your voice."

Before you embark upon your day, take a deep breath and tell yourself,
"Today I'm going to be heard! This is the day that my voice shall break through, this is the moment I break free from the shackles."

My Day /

_____
_____
_____
_____
_____
_____
_____
_____
_____
_____
_____

"Give yourself credit."

As you stand now think of the good you have done and give yourself a pat on the back for it. Any negative memories have served their educational purposes, it's now time to leave them in the past.

My Day /

_____
_____
_____
_____
_____
_____
_____
_____
_____
_____
_____

"Fulfill your promise."

There is no point being remembered as a contender baby, if you have the skills then get them working, turn them into something special. Fulfill the promise you have made to yourself.

My Day /

_____
_____
_____
_____
_____
_____
_____
_____
_____
_____
_____
_____

"Be a sponge."

Learn on the job, online, from books.....watch, absorb and grow. If you are a practicer, then practice, do what you need to do to go where you want to go. We are on a forever growing path, and self development is our greatest pleasure and our greatest asset.

My Day /

_____

_____

_____

_____

_____

_____

_____

_____

_____

_____

_____

"Master your domain."

Learn your craft and absorb knowledge on it until you achieve 'master' level. Perfect your technique to your highest standard and continue to adapt with changing times. If we are to be the best we must behave as the best.

My Day /

_____
_____
_____
_____
_____
_____
_____
_____
_____
_____
_____

"Stabilize your frequency."

Be consistent with the message you portray, the standards you have set are the standards you must want to deliver. Ensure people know what to expect as a consistent minimum from you.

My Day /

_____
_____
_____
_____
_____
_____
_____
_____
_____
_____
_____
_____

"Tomorrow starts today."

There are only so many times you can put it off till tomorrow, either you end up not doing it at all or tomorrow has to become today! Why wait anyway, why delay your future joys, why delay on the chasing of your dream for one day more?

My Day /

_____
_____
_____
_____
_____
_____
_____
_____
_____
_____
_____

"Discover the pathway."

At times you feel as though you hit one roadblock after another, but keep trying, persistence will uncover your way through. If you keep on pushing eventually something gives way, and behind it lies your passage to success.

My Day /

_____
_____
_____
_____
_____
_____
_____
_____
_____
_____
_____

"Evaluate what matters."

You have to evaluate what matters most, who and what will aid your progress, and what is the most crucial way to concentrate my efforts. Creating and managing your priorities will always be a key factor in the speed of your progress......so sharpen the saw before applying the blade.

My Day /

_____
_____
_____
_____
_____
_____
_____
_____
_____
_____
_____

"Become a terrier."

Your quest for knowledge should be equal to a terrier chasing down a scent, you must become unshakeable, pursuing your Goal with all your might. Leave no stone uncovered, no question unanswered.

My Day /

_____
_____
_____
_____
_____
_____
_____
_____
_____
_____
_____

"Set periodic milestones."

Have your completion date in mind then work back to where you are today, break that into as many segments as you need, set the milestones you'll recognize.....and work your plan. Having these little reminders along the way simply confirms you are staying on track.

My Day /

_____
_____
_____
_____
_____
_____
_____
_____
_____
_____
_____

"Act or observe."

There are those of us who get actively involved, and there are those of us who watch the world go by.........which one best represents you? Sitting on the fence advising and criticizing others won't enhance YOUR dreams, it will only belittle theirs.

My Day /

_____

_____

_____

_____

_____

_____

_____

_____

_____

_____

_____

_____

"Enthusiasm engages others."

It is natural human chemistry that we are drawn towards enthusiastic people, people with a contagious energy that engulfs them, people who uplift the soul. Which one of these best describes you?

My Day /

_____
_____
_____
_____
_____
_____
_____
_____
_____
_____
_____

"Channel your energy."

When you have a sense of applied focus you will discover an energy that will push you through most barriers, a drive that will rapidly bring your Goals closer to your reach.

My Day /

_____
_____
_____
_____
_____
_____
_____
_____
_____
_____
_____

"Enlighten the flock."

Have you got a message you absolutely believe in, something worth sharing but scared to offer it up for question? Be brave, someone out there is waiting to hear what YOU have got to say.

My Day /

_____

_____

_____

_____

_____

_____

_____

_____

_____

_____

"Avoid mixed messages."

Be consistent in what you say AND what you do, do not say you are worthy of a chance without your actions taking it up when the opportunity knocks. Don't be caught out talking a great game whilst performing a bad one.

My Day /

_____
_____
_____
_____
_____
_____
_____
_____
_____
_____
_____

"Work the plan."

Once you've established the path you've been searching for, work it.....the ups and the downs, the storms and the sunshine, it's all in there but know you'll come through. Great plans lead to great jobs, learn the benefits and use them with regularity.

My Day /

_____
_____
_____
_____
_____
_____
_____
_____
_____
_____
_____
_____

"Create something unique."

If you can't create something unique, do something current in a unique way........nobody reinvented the wheel, but they have made better tyres!

My Day /

_____
_____
_____
_____
_____
_____
_____
_____
_____
_____
_____
_____
_____

"Adapt or diminish."

Times are changing in seconds now, technology, information, opinions.......if you are able to adjust the sails at short notice, you'll steer clear of stormy weather.

My Day /

_____
_____
_____
_____
_____
_____
_____
_____
_____
_____
_____

"Manage your time."

People complain "they don't have the time", you do have the time, it's how you prioritize it. If you have time to watch Netflix, you have time to invest in your own growth. Don't let your time be withered away sitting on a sofa pondering, make things happen, activity is the key.

My Day /

_____
_____
_____
_____
_____
_____
_____
_____
_____
_____
_____

"Grasp the message."

If we keep our ears and eyes open we'll avoid wandering aimlessly through our days, picking up the little messages that lead to our bigger story. It's amazing how much we absorb when we least expect it.......and remember, not all lessons are done in the classroom!

My Day /

_____
_____
_____
_____
_____
_____
_____
_____
_____
_____
_____

"Normal is boring."

It's ok to be 'different', to be unique in your own special way, to have that distinctive aura that was reserved solely for YOU! Don't feel you have to fit in or conform to the ordinary, you are special and always be proud of your individuality.

My Day /

_____
_____
_____
_____
_____
_____
_____
_____
_____
_____
_____
_____

"Ride the waves."

If you can learn to ride the waves when the storm kicks up you'll be able to basque in the sunshine when the water runs smooth once again. Anyway, where would lie the excitement if it was plain sailing all of the time.

My Day /

_____
_____
_____
_____
_____
_____
_____
_____
_____
_____
_____
_____

"Better your yesterday's."

You can do it your way, and to do so you only have to be better tomorrow than YOU were today. YOU are the only one in this race you are up against. Daily progress wins the prize......gradual, steady, consistent growth........you'll be amazed at just how far it takes you.

My Day /

_____
_____
_____
_____
_____
_____
_____
_____
_____
_____
_____
_____

"Do it right."

There is no right way to get it wrong, and no wrong way to get it right, do the right things for the right reasons.........and you'll be all the happier for it.

My Day /

_____

_____

_____

_____

_____

_____

_____

_____

_____

_____

_____

_____

"Add your flavor."

Just as a chef does to a recipe, add that final ingredient that makes the ordinary that little bit special, add your unique touch to create a special flavor.

My Day /

_____
_____
_____
_____
_____
_____
_____
_____
_____
_____
_____
_____

"Create a momentum."

Get something going, give it energy, show enthusiasm, drive through a momentum that makes a worthy difference.

My Day /

_____
_____
_____
_____
_____
_____
_____
_____
_____
_____
_____

"Generate healthy routines."

To progress readily we must set healthy routines in ALL of our behaviors. If you're lazy in the home, you'll be lazy in the workplace. Set out with a thought, "what can I do today to ensure at least one more step towards my Goal?".

My Day /

"Value self discipline."

You have to take ownership of your own rule book, you are the motivator behind your daily planning, you will get out what you put in. Create little habits, set them into your life, then gradually change a few more.......positivity will come to you, one step at a time.

My Day /

_____
_____
_____
_____
_____
_____
_____
_____
_____
_____
_____
_____

"Question your progress."

What is worthy of your time, and what is crucial? Where are you investing in growing the life you want and what are you doing differently today from any other that's passed?

My Day /

_____
_____
_____
_____
_____
_____
_____
_____
_____
_____
_____

"Measure your input."

Many of us work on our dream 'job' outside of our daily job, how much time can you dedicate to furthering your dream, how much are you putting in to your personal plan?

My Day /

_____
_____
_____
_____
_____
_____
_____
_____
_____
_____
_____

"Leave the box."

If you are to grow you must be prepared to stretch beyond the box you have learned to be secure in, you must push yourself beyond the boundaries of your comfort zone.

My Day /

_____
_____
_____
_____
_____
_____
_____
_____
_____
_____
_____
_____

"Carry the message."

You can be a courier, but what is the message you will carry........a negative tale or a positive pathway?

My Day /

_____
_____
_____
_____
_____
_____
_____
_____
_____
_____
_____
_____

"Face your failings."

It's easier to basque in the glory of success but facing your failures is where your learning will be done. Don't turn your back on them, face them head on.

My Day /

"Understand the difference."

Understanding the value of the outcome of any situation will determine the lesson, regardless of wether you have won or lost.

My Day /

_____
_____
_____
_____
_____
_____
_____
_____
_____
_____
_____
_____

"Set new goals."

Regardless of wether you are currently winning or losing you must be aware of plateauing, that leveling off where you accept you are there. It may be time to move the goal posts once more, time for you to now raise the bar.

My Day /

_____
_____
_____
_____
_____
_____
_____
_____
_____
_____
_____
_____

"Want it more."

You have to keep moving every day, picking yourself up, out running and out fighting everyone on show.......giving your very best you are capable of that day! Everything we do in life allows us the chance of example.....what is the example we are showing, what are we displaying that shows that we simply want it more?

My Day /

_____
_____
_____
_____
_____
_____
_____
_____
_____
_____
_____
_____

"Try another door."

We've all felt the door slam in our face before but that only confirms this one is not our entry point.......that this was not the chance we had hoped it would be. However, it may just be that the very next one is the one we've been waiting for!

My Day /

_____
_____
_____
_____
_____
_____
_____
_____
_____
_____
_____

"Don't stop kicking."

The most successful swimmers are the ones who swim right to the finishing line, the ones who don't slow up until they have surged to the winners post and the cheers have gone up.

My Day /

_____
_____
_____
_____
_____
_____
_____
_____
_____
_____
_____

"Hear the cheers."

Do you envisage the joy of success, do you hear the cheers or see your name on the billboards, have you reached out and touched the feeling of success? See it, feel it, trust it, you can reach the greatest of heights.

My Day /

_____
_____
_____
_____
_____
_____
_____
_____
_____
_____
_____

"See yourself there."

I cannot stress enough how you must visualize yourself already there, in that dream role, enveloped in your moment of reaching the peak, being who you aim to be.

My Day /

_____
_____
_____
_____
_____
_____
_____
_____
_____
_____
_____
_____

"Smell the roses."

Try to take a second to embrace the small moments in your day, the little special occasions that touch your heart. Too often you later realize just how big some of them really were. Cherish them, so you'll remember them.

My Day /

_____
_____
_____
_____
_____
_____
_____
_____
_____
_____
_____
_____

"What matters most?"

What matters most to you, what is key to you in your progressive growth? Is it spiritual, economic, personal stature.......a question only YOU can answer? This journey is one with the outcomes held in only your own imagination.

My Day /

_____
_____
_____
_____
_____
_____
_____
_____
_____
_____
_____
_____

"Listen without interruption."

There are times when we must listen with intent, really hear what is being said......and sometimes what is not. There is a message not only in people's actions, but in their inaction too.

My Day /

_____
_____
_____
_____
_____
_____
_____
_____
_____
_____
_____

"Seize the opportunity."

If you are looking for that big break, still searching for your big chance, trust in that it WILL come to you, the door WILL open. And so, prepare yourself to be ready, ready to pounce and grab on with both hands.

My Day /

_____
_____
_____
_____
_____
_____
_____
_____
_____
_____
_____

"Climb the stairs."

Getting to the top is not just about the reward but about who you turn in to as you make your ascent. What you will learn along the way and possibly, who else you can take along with you for the ride.

My Day /

_____
_____
_____
_____
_____
_____
_____
_____
_____
_____
_____
_____

"What, when, why?"

Ask yourself these three questions as regularly as you can, as this is where your purpose rests, the purpose that will carry you over the obstacles you may well come to face. Knowing these three pointers will give you a sense of understanding, something you can hold on to when you are most in need.

My Day /

_____
_____
_____
_____
_____
_____
_____
_____
_____
_____
_____

"What makes me?"

You will reach crossroads many a time in your journey, and so you must evaluate what questions your principles, your belief system and your honor.........who will you be proud to become?

My Day /

_____
_____
_____
_____
_____
_____
_____
_____
_____
_____
_____
_____

"YOU lead you."

You are your own leader, you control your own destiny. The walk you take and the paths you'll travel, they will each be of your choosing, and ultimately, your choosing alone.

My Day /

_____
_____
_____
_____
_____
_____
_____
_____
_____
_____
_____
_____

"Each day differs."

We understand that every day we won't be at our peak, we may be feeling low energy or troubled. In these testing times remember to take a breath, realign your thinking and your focus, and prepare fully for a new tomorrow.

My Day /

_____
_____
_____
_____
_____
_____
_____
_____
_____
_____
_____
_____

"Enjoy the ride."

The thrill of a rollercoaster lies not only in the 'ups' but also in the 'downs' so learn to appreciate all of the ride and get used to some of the twists and turns that may come your way. And remember, you didn't get on to stop half way round.

My Day /

_____
_____
_____
_____
_____
_____
_____
_____
_____
_____
_____

"Broaden your expectations."

If you are to achieve more in life you must first heighten the levels of your expectation, raising your personal bar, believing you can step up another rung on the ladder. Don't restrict your ambitions, begin to expect more and your subconscious shall lead you there.

My Day /

_____
_____
_____
_____
_____
_____
_____
_____
_____
_____
_____

"Build your arsenal."

The more strings to your bow the stronger your position is and the safer you'll be. Continue to learn, new ways of approach, new views to consider, new avenues to explore. Build your armory so that you may branch off in whatever direction your path leads you, safe in the knowledge you're well equipped for the change.

My Day /

_____
_____
_____
_____
_____
_____
_____
_____
_____
_____
_____
_____

"Hold on tight."

Sometimes it can be a bumpy road so be sure to buckle up and hang on in there, the destination is not too far ahead.

My Day /

_____
_____
_____
_____
_____
_____
_____
_____
_____
_____
_____
_____

"Comprehend the joy."

Feel the joy of your achievement, see yourself at the pinnacle of your goal and imagine what it would be like to hold that dream in your hands?

My Day /

_____
_____
_____
_____
_____
_____
_____
_____
_____
_____
_____
_____

"What's worth chasing?"

*What are you out there in search of, is what you pursue really worthy of your time and effort......
If not it's time to level up your Goal.*

My Day /

_____
_____
_____
_____
_____
_____
_____
_____
_____
_____
_____

"Time is limited."

Each milestone of your journey must also have a date beside it, a limiter to ensure you don't fall behind and begin to wander off track. Set dates, and stick to them!

My Day /

_____
_____
_____
_____
_____
_____
_____
_____
_____
_____
_____
_____

"Work your ticket."

Use your talent, whatever that gift is......work it, and do not stop until your breakthrough comes! There is no greater loss than talent that lies unused and no greater joy than the moment your dream becomes a reality.

My Day /

_____
_____
_____
_____
_____
_____
_____
_____
_____
_____
_____
_____

"What drives you?"

What gets you going, what is it that pushes your effort level up that extra notch?
When you find it, harness it.......keep it deep in your stomach, and use it whenever the need falls.

My Day /

_____
_____
_____
_____
_____
_____
_____
_____
_____
_____
_____

"Review your routines."

From the earliest hour to the last flicker of light, make sure you are practicing good habits. Manage your day and all that goes in it, making changes as needs require. Daily routines make a world of difference, the enthusiasm shown in making your bed in the morning will be the same enthusiasm you bring in to your other daily activities.

My Day /

_____
_____
_____
_____
_____
_____
_____
_____
_____
_____
_____
_____

"Validate the reason."

Keep reminding yourself "why" you are doing what you are doing, what is your purpose, what are the gains? The benefits in this for you or yours will provide a lift when you need it most. Your personal reasons should drive you, it should stand as the fuel in your tank.

My Day /

_____
_____
_____
_____
_____
_____
_____
_____
_____
_____
_____

"Deafen the doubters."

There will be a doubter on hand for many steps of your journey, but the only person who's view is entirely relevant here is YOURS! Don't be sucked in by insignificant opinions, they simply will not matter as your story unfolds.

My Day /

_____
_____
_____
_____
_____
_____
_____
_____
_____
_____
_____

"Determine the result."

You have the power to adjust the sails if it's not going right, you have the power to forge ahead when it's going well. Do not lament, make the days count and construct the results that matter most to you.

My Day /

_____
_____
_____
_____
_____
_____
_____
_____
_____
_____
_____
_____

"I remain flexible."

People's bodies, and minds, stiffen up when not used, regardless of age or position.......retain your flexibility and you will last the marathon of life.

My Day /

_____
_____
_____
_____
_____
_____
_____
_____
_____
_____
_____

"Experience becomes wisdom."

We 'learn on the job' of life, and whilst there is no prerequisite for some of the experiences we will endure, we know they will teach us, good and bad, how to grow.

My Day /

_____

_____

_____

_____

_____

_____

_____

_____

_____

_____

_____

"Release your garbage."

If you continue to carry unnecessary baggage it will eventually weigh you down and slow up the progress that you are trying to make. Do not punish yourself by carrying the negative garbage you've collected through your daily life, throw in the trash what deserves to be there.

My Day /

_____
_____
_____
_____
_____
_____
_____
_____
_____
_____
_____
_____

"Evolve through life."

We have to adapt, and adapt quickly, learn to adjust to the differing Worlds we experience with age. Dinosaurs are nowhere to be found with good reason, don't make their mistakes, don't avoid change but instead, learn to embrace it.

My Day /

_____
_____
_____
_____
_____
_____
_____
_____
_____
_____
_____

"Widen your viewpoint."

Our focus should be direct but our minds remain open, otherwise our own opinion becomes our only consideration and our learning is removed.

My Day /

_____
_____
_____
_____
_____
_____
_____
_____
_____
_____
_____
_____

"Understand the relevance."

Many of the teachings we experience can flatten our mood, but without them we will not learn and without learning we will not grow. See it for what it is, no more, no less.

My Day /

_____
_____
_____
_____
_____
_____
_____
_____
_____
_____
_____
_____

"Focus is paramount."

Regardless of the job at hand we must apply ourselves fully to get it right on Q. Remind yourself frequently where you are headed, you are the internal map of your own journey.

My Day /

_____
_____
_____
_____
_____
_____
_____
_____
_____
_____
_____

"Time to reflect?"

Even if it's only once a month, take some time out to reflect on how you're doing. By stopping to give yourself proper thinking periods you'll consistently review how far you've travelled.

My Day /

_____
_____
_____
_____
_____
_____
_____
_____
_____
_____
_____
_____
_____

"Don't run away."

How often have we wanted to bury our heads and avoid facing problems? It's a natural instinct, but bad news must be told early, and avoid carrying it on your back too long.

My Day /

_____
_____
_____
_____
_____
_____
_____
_____
_____
_____
_____

"Raise your eyeline."

Stop looking at the ground, get your head up, mistakes are part of our journey but they are not the only page to be read out loud.......there is many an applause still yet to be had.

My Day /

_____
_____
_____
_____
_____
_____
_____
_____
_____
_____
_____

"Break some sweat."

It's not going to happen by itself you know, YOU are the one who will make the difference, YOU are the one where the buck of your Goals finally stops.

My Day /

_____
_____
_____
_____
_____
_____
_____
_____
_____
_____
_____
_____

"Magnify your dream."

Don't short change yourself, do not belittle your dream due to doubts or questioning your own self worth. YOU are worthy of whatever you allow yourself to believe in, go for it!

My Day /

_____
_____
_____
_____
_____
_____
_____
_____
_____
_____
_____
_____
_____

"Review daily habits."

If what you are doing is not taking you where you want to go, improve your daily habits.....from the very smallest detail to the largest deal of the day. Only by improving what we once did will we go where we've never been.

My Day /

_____
_____
_____
_____
_____
_____
_____
_____
_____
_____
_____
_____

"Time drifts away."

How often do we put off the job at hand, how frequently will we misuse and devalue OUR own time? That sand is flowing through your personal egg timer, get moving before your time of chance finally runs out.

My Day /

_____
_____
_____
_____
_____
_____
_____
_____
_____
_____
_____
_____
_____

"Register a commitment."

Until you write it down, until you set a date, the dream remains a dream and not a commitment. Come on, do yourself no more disservice, get some dates in the diary, let's fill in your journal of Goals.

My Day /

_____
_____
_____
_____
_____
_____
_____
_____
_____
_____
_____
_____

"Lay the tracks"

Make a personal deal for the next 6 months of your life, lay out a plan before you that you can work from and clearly comprehend.......let's get those wheels turning.

My Day /

_____
_____
_____
_____
_____
_____
_____
_____
_____
_____
_____
_____
_____

"Needs restrict choices."

Our immediate needs and priorities may necessitate holding down the job or position we are currently in, so how do we find the time to work on our dream? We may have to find additional time not replacing time, we may have to put in additional hours to work on our dream whilst we currently work on our living. Find the time, it'll be worth it for sure.

My Day /

_____
_____
_____
_____
_____
_____
_____
_____
_____
_____
_____

"Hope carries us."

We will always be in the fight for as long as we can retain hope. Hope is the thing that engages those who will kick the door down just one more time in search of the light that lies beyond it. Hope is the very thing that will see us over the line when all seems lost.

My Day /

_____
_____
_____
_____
_____
_____
_____
_____
_____
_____
_____
_____

"Perfection takes time."

What would happen if a baby stopped trying to walk at the first fall? Babies don't yet understand failure or success, they only understand need. Are you able to get back up and try again or will you give up after only the second or third attempt?

My Day /

_____
_____
_____
_____
_____
_____
_____
_____
_____
_____
_____

"Water continuously flows."

The greatest power of water is that it doesn't stop, its strength lies in its persistence and movement.......if there is a passageway it will find it and continue to move forward. If you can embody this theory, this never say die attitude, you too shall find route to your ocean.

My Day /

_____
_____
_____
_____
_____
_____
_____
_____
_____
_____
_____
_____

"Fill the pages."

We start each day with a brand new page, an opportunity to create a new chapter and to change the plot if needs must. This is YOUR book, write it to suit YOUR story.

My Day /

_____
_____
_____
_____
_____
_____
_____
_____
_____
_____
_____
_____

"Develop your negatives."

As photographers have shown us many times, the most beautiful pictures started as negatives. What you see depends largely on how you look at it.

My Day /

_____
_____
_____
_____
_____
_____
_____
_____
_____
_____
_____

"Run YOUR race."

This is your race to run, and it's to be ran at your own pace. Apply the focus to where your finishing line lies and calculate what is needed from YOU to achieve your best time.

My Day /

_____

_____

_____

_____

_____

_____

_____

_____

_____

_____

_____

"Domino's will fall."

One of the greatest shifts you will experience is momentum, that joyous moment when the dominoes finally start to run and you feel the thrill of continuous achievement.

My Day /

_____
_____
_____
_____
_____
_____
_____
_____
_____
_____
_____

"Perception manipulates choices."

How any of us see something will ultimately determine our decision making. If you want someone to jump on your bus, you will first have to see it through THEIR eyes.

My Day /

_____
_____
_____
_____
_____
_____
_____
_____
_____
_____
_____

"Visualize the outcome."

What you are doing RIGHT NOW, where is that taking you, where are you going to finish up if you continue on the current track? What must be done to reach your ultimate Goals?

My Day /

_____

_____

_____

_____

_____

_____

_____

_____

_____

_____

_____

_____

"Worry yields little."

Worry is born out of inactivity, a paralyzing fear of things that often never materialize. If you can change something to remove this feeling, do it.....if you can't, move on.

My Day /

_____
_____
_____
_____
_____
_____
_____
_____
_____
_____
_____
_____

"Progress is progress."

Some days you may feel it's a struggle just to get one foot in front of the other, but even when it's baby steps, you're still moving forward!

My Day /

"Get yourself moving."

No Goal was ever met by simply talking about it, eventually you've got to get up and get going. It will not happen by itself, you must be the driver that gets the engine started.

My Day /

_____
_____
_____
_____
_____
_____
_____
_____
_____
_____
_____

"Count your steps."

Isn't it amazing how enthusiastic we all are to monitor our daily steps on our watches but not in the progress of our lives? Who's keeping score on your Goal?

My Day /

_____
_____
_____
_____
_____
_____
_____
_____
_____
_____
_____
_____

"Reject the rejection."

Rejection saves time in many ways, it permits you to move along a little bit quicker and brings you that little bit closer to the 'YES' you so desperately crave. Accept it for what it is but don't allow it to weaken your spirit......shoulders back, chest out, and go again.

My Day /

_____
_____
_____
_____
_____
_____
_____
_____
_____
_____
_____
_____

"Provide a solution."

Every successful business is built upon serving somebody's needs, and every good friend knows the best way to support the troubles of another. Know the purpose of the path you are traveling and know when to put your input across.

My Day /

_____
_____
_____
_____
_____
_____
_____
_____
_____
_____
_____

"Rekindle the flame."

With every setback there can come increased doubt, but this can be precisely your opportune time to reevaluate your proposal, and maybe just the right time to throw some extra fuel on the fire to reignite that internal flame.

My Day /

_____
_____
_____
_____
_____
_____
_____
_____
_____
_____
_____
_____

"Determination overcomes adversity."

That drive to succeed, that determination to fulfill your promise, is entirely what will ensure you overcome any adversity thrown at you and what brings you to the top of the pile. Believing wholeheartedly in the dream you are following will be the catalyst for your success.

My Day /

_____
_____
_____
_____
_____
_____
_____
_____
_____
_____
_____
_____

"Take another route."

If the the rocks begin to tumble and the road through becomes blocked, seek out another way. Your journey doesn't end here, it's just time to try another route.

My Day /

_____
_____
_____
_____
_____
_____
_____
_____
_____
_____
_____

"Drive your Day."

Get up early, outline a plan or timetable, make your day productive from the very first off. It's so easy to lose a day with inactivity, but YOU simply can't entertain that notion.

My Day /

_____
_____
_____
_____
_____
_____
_____
_____
_____
_____
_____
_____

"What's to compare."

It is easy to find ourselves comparing where we're at with others, but remember, the only person's progress that really matters is our own! Your biggest competitor is staring you back in the mirror, you are the only one who's days you must compare.

My Day /

_____
_____
_____
_____
_____
_____
_____
_____
_____
_____
_____

"Engage your Goal."

Set your Goal out before you and get to work on bringing it to life. We each have 24 hours, we must make the space in our lives to breathe life into our dreams. Once you commit yourself to achieving a Goal you'll be amazed at how quickly the path through begins to materialize.

My Day /

_____
_____
_____
_____
_____
_____
_____
_____
_____
_____
_____
_____

"Advance your position."

Are you where you expected to be, are you deserved of a higher place.......be honest with yourself, are you where your efforts merit or need you do more?

My Day /

_____
_____
_____
_____
_____
_____
_____
_____
_____
_____
_____

"Do what matters."

It's a very fine line between doing what you want to be doing and doing what you need to be doing, but to be able to do the first sometimes you first have to excel in the second.

My Day /

_____
_____
_____
_____
_____
_____
_____
_____
_____
_____
_____

"Embody a freshness."

What stands out about you, what makes you memorable, why will people wish to engage with you more than others.........will they see you as a breath of fresh air?!

My Day /

_____
_____
_____
_____
_____
_____
_____
_____
_____
_____
_____
_____

"Calmness influences thinking."

If you can give yourself adequate space to think, free from noise or distraction, you will be amazed at the clarity of your thoughts when calmness surrounds you.

My Day /

"Define your time."

What are you doing currently that defines you, what contribution are you making and what will be your epitaph when you're gone?

My Day /

_____
_____
_____
_____
_____
_____
_____
_____
_____
_____
_____

"Adjust the boundaries."

Do we genuinely push ourself outside our own comfort zone to experience more from life? Can we improve on that....not only in a monetary or material sense but in a spiritual one too?

My Day /

_____
_____
_____
_____
_____
_____
_____
_____
_____
_____
_____

"Own your choices."

Our choices in life, good and bad, are ours to own. We can't lay blame or credit at the door of another. If we can see life as our canvas we need only decide the colours we will throw at it.

My Day /

_____
_____
_____
_____
_____
_____
_____
_____
_____
_____
_____
_____

"Treadmills can stop."

Once we are on that treadmill of life we may find it a struggle to get off, however, we are not here to run uphill through life, we can choose another track.

My Day /

_____
_____
_____
_____
_____
_____
_____
_____
_____
_____
_____
_____

"Manage your expectations."

Humility can cause us to restrict our dreams, to not shoot high enough or truly believe we are worthy of a top prize. But it's there if we want it, we can too sit at the table of the chosen few.

My Day /

_____
_____
_____
_____
_____
_____
_____
_____
_____
_____
_____

"Restart the engine."

Once in a while stop and check things over, reassess situations and prepare for the next race. And the second that moment has arrived, turn that key and go beat down the track.

My Day /

_____
_____
_____
_____
_____
_____
_____
_____
_____
_____
_____
_____

"Change will come."

The one thing that is certain in life is change, good and bad, some you can control and some you can't. Our priority is to be able to adjust quickly, to be ready to flow with it, and move with speed.

My Day /

_____
_____
_____
_____
_____
_____
_____
_____
_____
_____
_____

"What works best?"

What are you doing now that is most productive and what are you doing over and over that is not? You know what one has to go to allow the other to flourish!

My Day /

_____
_____
_____
_____
_____
_____
_____
_____
_____
_____
_____

"Complete the task."

Don't be known as 'a good starter', get the job(s) done accordingly and don't move on with a job half done. It's good personal management to complete tasks before accepting the next one.

My Day /

_____
_____
_____
_____
_____
_____
_____
_____
_____
_____
_____

"Set good examples."

People are watching you when you least expect it.......children, colleagues, friends......there are people who hold YOU in high esteem and look to see if YOU'LL do it right.

My Day /

_____
_____
_____
_____
_____
_____
_____
_____
_____
_____
_____
_____

"Create personal milestones."

Set limits that kick you into gear, trigger points that tell you it's time to get things moving and when you've crossed a line on route. It may be work related, exercise, study.......whatever it is, know when to get going on the next stage of your Goal.

My Day /

_____
_____
_____
_____
_____
_____
_____
_____
_____
_____
_____

"Find a way."

There's always a way to get the job done, a path yet unseen or an idea that has not been considered. Keep searching for the door that opens, find your way through to the promised land.

My Day /

_____
_____
_____
_____
_____
_____
_____
_____
_____
_____
_____

"Words kill spirits."

Be careful what you say and how you say it, even to yourself. Your words are powerful and can drain the enthusiasm or inject it, be aware of their impact before you open your mouth.

My Day /

_____
_____
_____
_____
_____
_____
_____
_____
_____
_____
_____
_____

"Explore new horizons."

Take the leap of faith, discover what lies out there that you have yet to touch. There is a difference between using 7 days of the week and repeating 1 day of the week 7 times........!

My Day /

_____
_____
_____
_____
_____
_____
_____
_____
_____
_____
_____

"What's your motivator?"

Is there something, or someone, in your life that serves as your key motivator? Or is it entirely personal, is it a childhood dream held on to that flourishes you with joy when your thoughts drift upon it? Whatever it is, use it, make it the driver that pushes you forward when you need it most.

My Day /

_____
_____
_____
_____
_____
_____
_____
_____
_____
_____
_____

"Influence the moment."

What can YOU contribute, what difference will your input make? Consider YOUR options, your words and your actions, your personal contribution could just make the world of difference!

My Day /

_____

_____

_____

_____

_____

_____

_____

_____

_____

_____

_____

"Set the pace."

Can YOU be the lead runner, can you be the guiding light for those around you to follow? Simple things make a big difference, you just never know the influence you could have on others needing a little inspiration.

My Day /

_____

_____

_____

_____

_____

_____

_____

_____

_____

_____

_____

"React without force."

Other people's buy in comes when they understand the personal benefits, not when they understand yours! Don't force what can be discussed, see it from their perspective, and show them you understand their needs first before asking them to buy into yours.

My Day /

_____
_____
_____
_____
_____
_____
_____
_____
_____
_____
_____
_____

"Eyes display souls."

Although we ask others how they may be, do we really look beyond the question, do we search for the deeper answer? Be kind when you can, you never know the benefit your actions could have on another.

My Day /

_____
_____
_____
_____
_____
_____
_____
_____
_____
_____
_____
_____

"Who's watching who?"

On every ladder in life there is a way up and a way down, and on each rung lies a person.....
So always be aware, whilst you are looking at YOUR pier, someone is looking at you as theirs.

My Day /

_____
_____
_____
_____
_____
_____
_____
_____
_____
_____
_____
_____

"Swing the mood."

When you see the mood around you falling can you instrument a positive change, can you lift the spirit of others and most importantly, can you lift your own?

My Day /

_____
_____
_____
_____
_____
_____
_____
_____
_____
_____
_____

"Where to next?"

Are you challenging yourself with this question or are you repeating your days and weeks? What is on your agenda, what difference are your current plans going to make to your journey?

My Day /

_____
_____
_____
_____
_____
_____
_____
_____
_____
_____
_____

"What's the message?"

When we've had an off day, or even a singular situation that's stopped us in our tracks, it's always worth asking ourselves this very important question, ie 'what can I learn here?'.

My Day /

_____
_____
_____
_____
_____
_____
_____
_____
_____
_____
_____

"Avoid self pity."

It's all too easy to let knocks get us down but it only delays progress and flattens our mood. Dust yourself down and get back up, this is not the end of the road my friend.

My Day /

_____

_____

_____

_____

_____

_____

_____

_____

_____

_____

_____

"Bridges link people."

Are you the bridge, are you the connector of people? We can each be a link in the chain, we can each make an effort to bring together those who need it most.

My Day /

_____
_____
_____
_____
_____
_____
_____
_____
_____
_____
_____

"Appreciate and attract."

When you are in a true state of appreciation you radiate a magnetic attraction that brings greater experiences and positivity in abundance......focus on your feelings before you start your day.

My Day /

_____
_____
_____
_____
_____
_____
_____
_____
_____
_____
_____

"Clear the path."

It is easy to accumulate debris along the way but instead of it being in our past it becomes the blockage of our future........be rid of it, clear the way ahead.

My Day /

_____
_____
_____
_____
_____
_____
_____
_____
_____
_____
_____

"Leave survival mode."

It's difficult to build a dream when day to day you are just trying to survive. Investigate what excites you most, invest any possible spare time in your dream, any spare second apply to the future YOU.

My Day /

_____
_____
_____
_____
_____
_____
_____
_____
_____
_____
_____
_____

"Fill the cup."

People compare having a half empty cup or half full, but if you can fill it all the way up will this really matter? No half measures, go the whole way, fill it to the brim.

My Day /

_____
_____
_____
_____
_____
_____
_____
_____
_____
_____
_____

"Use the platform."

When that light shines upon you and you raise yourself to the platform, grab the opportunity to shine with both hands and give the performance of your life.

My Day /

_____
_____
_____
_____
_____
_____
_____
_____
_____
_____
_____
_____

"Mentors change lives."

Having a mentor can aid you in constructing a better life and being a mentor can aid someone else in improving theirs.

My Day /

_____
_____
_____
_____
_____
_____
_____
_____
_____
_____
_____

"Ambition always matters."

Our ambitions may vary, from changes in time or changes in circumstance, but with us they shall remain, for they represent our very essence of hope.

My Day /

_____
_____
_____
_____
_____
_____
_____
_____
_____
_____
_____
_____

"Wake up excited."

Does what you are currently doing have you excited from dawn till dark, are you desperate to get started on another day building your dream? There are no dress rehearsals, this is it, be that you cannot wait to get started on a brand new day.

My Day /

_____
_____
_____
_____
_____
_____
_____
_____
_____
_____
_____

"Lose the distractions."

Throughout our lives distractions will come in differing guises. Prioritize what comes first, what MUST I do to take my Goal forward? Lose the fog and clarify your focus on what matters most. Do what you need to do to get you where your want to go.

My Day /

_____
_____
_____
_____
_____
_____
_____
_____
_____
_____
_____
_____

"I and me."

Are you an 'I and Me' or a 'We and Us'? Be honest with yourself, where do you fit in, or do you wish to fit in at all? Know who you are, it'll save you time and help your clarity in who you wish to become.

My Day /

_____
_____
_____
_____
_____
_____
_____
_____
_____
_____
_____

"Overcome the struggles."

People say struggles build characters but that can be easier said than done, when you're there it's tough. Look for support groups, gain a mentor, ask for help from those who have made it, it will ease the struggle and share the weight.

My Day /

_____
_____
_____
_____
_____
_____
_____
_____
_____
_____
_____
_____

"Who supports most?"

Who is your shoulder to cry on, who is your rock who will assist you on the road? Friends and family that can be truly relied upon are rare, so when you find them, value them, and keep them close.

My Day /

_____
_____
_____
_____
_____
_____
_____
_____
_____
_____
_____

"Encapsulate inner determination."

Resilience, determination, courage, these are all the words of the fight that we'll need to walk the coals and make it to the other side. Lift your chin, hold self belief in your heart and get ready to march ahead.

My Day /

_____
_____
_____
_____
_____
_____
_____
_____
_____
_____
_____

"Discredit no one."

Our priority is to be measured by what we contribute. There is no space to grow by discrediting another, that has no place in our journey! This is about our development not another's destruction.

My Day /

_____
_____
_____
_____
_____
_____
_____
_____
_____
_____
_____

"Fact over fiction."

Don't believe everything you read in the papers, and don't take everyone's opinion as fact. Do your own research, uncover the information YOU require.....for you are your own journalist in life.

My Day /

_____
_____
_____
_____
_____
_____
_____
_____
_____
_____
_____

"Control the content."

What's your message, what are you trying to say to others? Are you aware of the package you are, what you represent and who you are trying to grow in to? Value who and what you stand for, stand by the content of your story and feel proud of both the ups AND the downs.

My Day /

_____
_____
_____
_____
_____
_____
_____
_____
_____
_____
_____

"Quieten the noise."

Many people now meditate, do yoga, pilates etc......all to find ways of 'quieting the noise' on a very personal basis. For each of us there is our very own way of finding this base, this place where we can each retreat to that allows us to rebalance. Whatever it is or means to you personally, find it, it will help you in controlling your thinking as well as your direction.

My Day /

_____
_____
_____
_____
_____
_____
_____
_____
_____
_____
_____

"Spirit or Spirituality?"

We often hear people refer to our 'spirit' but not so much our spirituality. There can be a very real difference for many of us, sometimes involving our fight and our desire and other times involving our belief systems. Either way these are both private and helpful. Understanding what either means to YOU is important as well as how you can make them benefit you on a personal basis.

My Day /

_____
_____
_____
_____
_____
_____
_____
_____
_____
_____
_____

"Kindness really counts."

How far do you believe your kindness doth carry, do you believe it really matters? How do you feel when you display kindness and it goes both appreciated and unappreciated? Remember, this is about what YOU do, that is the only part YOU can truly control......In the words of Caroline Flack, if you can be anything, be kind.

My Day /

_____
_____
_____
_____
_____
_____
_____
_____
_____
_____
_____

"Communities unite people."

At the heart of any family or collective is the spirit of that community, the essence of what makes it special and the gratitude that carries through it. What contribution to that culture comes from YOU? What do you put in that supports it's longevity and it's passion, what can YOU do that enhances the group from its very core?

My Day /

_____
_____
_____
_____
_____
_____
_____
_____
_____
_____
_____
_____

"Uncover the strength."

It's in there, there is a fight inside of you that at times, will need to come out. If you come face on to a challenge what are your options going to be, which way will you turn? Dig a little deeper and you'll find it, and when you need it most, you'll come to rely on it.

My Day /

_____
_____
_____
_____
_____
_____
_____
_____
_____
_____
_____

"Implement the change."

Change comes to us in many guises, some we like, some we don't. But the one thing history has taught us is that change will come, and how we accommodate it will be all that matters come what may. See when change is necessary, understand it.......and if you can, be the one to implement it.

My Day /

_____
_____
_____
_____
_____
_____
_____
_____
_____
_____
_____

"Make the breakthrough."

I've experienced personally where I feel I've given all I've got, pushed at the door so many times and it just won't open........and then out of the blue comes the breakthrough I've been hoping for, and often from where I didn't expect it. Push a little further, you're nearly there.

My Day /

_____
_____
_____
_____
_____
_____
_____
_____
_____
_____
_____

"Beef it up."

What does your current skill set or resumé say about you, does it need beefing up? Are you self developing, are you learning new tricks to offer or to ensure you stand out from the crowd?
There is an abundance of information out there, reading videos, tutorials......there are no excuses left!

My Day /

_____
_____
_____
_____
_____
_____
_____
_____
_____
_____
_____

"Volunteer your assistance."

Volunteering your help can benefit you in so many ways. Sometimes when we are feeling low or struggling with gratitude getting out there and seeing who needs OUR help can remind us of the good fortune of where we are at. It can also demonstrate your enthusiasm to support others, a trait that never goes unnoticed in the workplace or in life.

My Day /

_____
_____
_____
_____
_____
_____
_____
_____
_____
_____
_____

"Record and reflect."

We must not only keep record of our progress but essentially, we must learn to regularly check it. If you are driving a lengthy distance and somewhere along the road you take the wrong turning, wouldn't you want to recognize your error as early as possible? Our mistakes in life are ok, so long as we make adjustments, learn from them, and then move on.

My Day /

_____
_____
_____
_____
_____
_____
_____
_____
_____
_____
_____

"Dream YOUR dream."

Are we living in a state of pursuit, are we really chasing our dreams? I ask myself this often, as it's so easy to get caught up in the daily treadmill of life, forgetting what your dream looks like or how you can bring it to life. Keep yourself on track, don't let your Goals slip through your fingers, keep reminding yourself of your hope and ambition......this is no trial run, this is our one chance to be who we want.

My Day /

_____
_____
_____
_____
_____
_____
_____
_____
_____
_____
_____
_____

"See the reward."

Visualization is incredibly important in the pursuit of our Goal(s). We must know why we are doing something, what is the reward and who is it for. That image must always serve as a timely reminder to us, especially in the darker days when our spirits are low. How we do this is completely personal, a photo, a wallpaper on screens......whatever it may be, position it where you can see it daily.

My Day /

_____
_____
_____
_____
_____
_____
_____
_____
_____
_____
_____
_____

"Who's the director?"

Who orchestrates your performance, who is in charge of what you are doing? Is it you, is it someone else, who's approval do you seek? This is YOUR stage remember, your opportunity to show your talents. Seek first self approval, be satisfied in the skills you wish to display, develop your uniqueness......and then forge ahead with the wind at your back.

My Day /

_____

_____

_____

_____

_____

_____

_____

_____

_____

_____

_____

"Toughen your tests."

There is no joy in victory where lies an easy opponent! Our personal growth will be based on the challenges we set for ourselves, the heights of our tests and the scale of our successes. Ask yourself if your progress is accelerating at a level you are happy with, or is it possibly now time to reassess your Goals?

My Day /

_____

_____

_____

_____

_____

_____

_____

_____

_____

_____

_____

"Accommodate your mistakes."

Mistakes will be made, we will have regrets, but if you can learn to understand them then you'll know truly where their benefits lie. Growth rarely comes without a stumble here and there, it's all part of the process and all part of life. Accommodate in your mind how best to handle setbacks and you'll waste little time dwelling on the past.

My Day /

_____
_____
_____
_____
_____
_____
_____
_____
_____
_____
_____

"Keep doing it."

It's well known that persistence will generally overcome all challenges or barriers. From the earliest age a child learns to keep asking until the parent finally gives in. And so it is to water, it keeps pressing till the dams are breached. Concentrate your flow, be the one who never gives in, reach the shores through sheer determination. You know if you keep fighting you'll definitely be the last one standing.

My Day /

_____
_____
_____
_____
_____
_____
_____
_____
_____
_____
_____

"Economize your energy."

As we get older we know when our bursts of energy are put to their very best use, we question more readily if we will run about aimlessly. Observe your mentors, how do they utilize their time to ensure the maximum return for it, what is it they do that sees progress from their actions where in others there is little? Use your time wisely and you'll understand it's value better.

My Day /

_____
_____
_____
_____
_____
_____
_____
_____
_____
_____
_____
_____
_____

"Seek the example."

I have always loved listening to successful people tell us their life stories, or read a hero's biography to discover the special ingredients they possess that we require. What is the key factor that runs throughout when I look at these people..........in each of them there lies the understanding and importance of being the great example, doing as they say and living what they believe.

My Day /

_____
_____
_____
_____
_____
_____
_____
_____
_____
_____
_____
_____

"Space lies available."

Regardless of how many have gone before you, or how many have already made it to the top of your personal mountain, there is always room for one more! In the years that have followed Roger Bannisters' sub 4 minute mile it has now been broken by over 1400 more athletes, do you think their achievement has any less value to them, is it any less of an accomplishment?!

My Day /

_____
_____
_____
_____
_____
_____
_____
_____
_____
_____
_____
_____

"Achievement over dollar."

Money comes and goes, it brings it's own joy and satisfaction, but it never quite replaces the feeling of accomplishment when a Goal has been met. What you will be remembered by is not measurable in monitory terms, it will come from the stamp you leave and the impression you've made on people. Take pride in that, and consider it as you go.

My Day /

_____
_____
_____
_____
_____
_____
_____
_____
_____
_____
_____

"Oil the chain."

Keep the mind and body moving, do not allow rust to gather on any of the links, make sure the chain is taught and you're fit for the race. The greatest risk to us all is complacency, thinking we are already there when we may still be a few yards short. We're in for the long game remember, not for one isolated race, but for the whole season of events.

My Day /

_____
_____
_____
_____
_____
_____
_____
_____
_____
_____
_____

"I have value."

Love must start with you, for you, within you and of you. Understand the basis of your value and of the qualities that are so unique and that simply make you.......you! You have worked hard to be who you are, so don't give it away too easily, find your own place of inner contentment, and all the key reasons why you are so worthy of simply being YOU.

My Day /

_____
_____
_____
_____
_____
_____
_____
_____
_____
_____
_____

"Solve the puzzle."

As the challenge of the puzzle faces you will you apply the necessary thinking to overcome the test, will you retain the willpower to move beyond the hills that will surely come your way? If you can learn to enjoy the differing routes of the path the way ahead shall clear and the winners post shall await you.

My Day /

_____
_____
_____
_____
_____
_____
_____
_____
_____
_____
_____

"Now look back."

So this is the time to reflect on your year, to look back over these pages and see how it's gone. Are you where you thought you'd be, are you further ahead, or have you still a little bit of the way still to go? Wherever you are, be sure you've enjoyed it and learned a lot along the way.
Try to view it more as what you've gained rather than what you've lost.

My Day /

_____
_____
_____
_____
_____
_____
_____
_____
_____
_____
_____
_____

"Now look forward."

Take what you've gained and now look ahead to what comes next. Where are you going now, what are your plans for the next 365 days and have you got to up your game from the days that have now settled in the past? Make plans now, get ready for some new Goals, and for continuance of some current ones..........and go smash a brand new year!

My Day /

_____
_____
_____
_____
_____
_____
_____
_____
_____
_____
_____
_____

Milton Keynes UK
Ingram Content Group UK Ltd.
UKHW020644120124
435917UK00015B/535

9 781916 981430